5⁰⁰

David Spitzenberger
3902 Sumac
Temple, TX 76502
773-2600 — 778-3222

D1627322

CREATIVE MATHEMATICS

Creative Mathematics

This book is not a compendium of mathematical facts and inventions to be read over as a connoisseur of art looks over paintings in a gallery. It is, instead, a sketchbook in which the reader may try his hand at mathematical discovery.

BY H. S. WALL

UNIVERSITY OF TEXAS PRESS · AUSTIN

Library of Congress Catalog Card No. 63-7439
Copyright © 1963 H. S. Wall
Printed in the United States of America

To All Creative Thinkers Everywhere

PREFACE

This book is intended to lead the student to develop his mathematical ability, to help him learn the art of mathematics, to teach him to create mathematical ideas. This is not a compendium of mathematical facts and inventions to be read over as a connoisseur of art looks over the paintings in a gallery. It is, instead, a sketchbook in which the reader may try his hand at mathematical discovery.

The American painter Winslow Homer is said to have declared that painters should not look at the works of others for fear of damaging their own directness of expression. I believe the same is true of the mathematician. The fresher the approach the better—there is less to unlearn; there are fewer bad thinking habits to overcome. In my teaching experience, some of my best students have been among those who entered my classes with the least previous mathematical course work. On the other hand, I have usually found it very difficult, if not impossible, to get any kind of creative effort from a student who has had many poor courses in mathematics. This has been true in some cases even though, as it developed later on, the student had very unusual mathematical ability.

The development of mathematical ability is a long-term proposition. There are no short cuts. This book is written for the person who seeks an intellectual challenge and who can find genuine pleasure in spending hours and even weeks in constructing proofs for the theorems of one chapter or even a portion of one chapter. It is a book which may be useful for the formal student and which is also intended for the person who is not in school but who wants to study mathematics on his own. A person who has worked through this book can be regarded as a good mathematician.

Much mathematical jargon, to some of which any but the most unspoiled person has been exposed, has very little real meaning. For instance, the statement found in most algebra books that "a quadratic equation may have real and equal roots" is pure nonsense. Unnecessary or meaningless adjectives form a part of this jargon. For instance, there is no such thing as a *small* positive number, let alone an *arbitrarily small* positive number or an *arbitrarily small pre-assigned* positive number.

In this book, I have tried to say exactly what I mean according to my best understanding of the English language. There are fine shades of meaning in the language used. The *little* words are especially important. For example, if a man says "I have *a* son," it is not to be assumed that he does not have two sons. Thus, in this book, a set which contains ten objects contains one object and may contain twenty objects. Incidentally, the part of that aforementioned jargon which speaks of *the empty set* has no place here !

I have tried to avoid unnecessary names for things and unnecessary symbols. The attachment to a theorem of the names of persons in some way associated with it might prevent someone from attempting to prove it. For example, imagine a beginner who would not be in awe of "The Bolzano-Weierstrass Theorem." Also, a word or symbol which is a substitute for an idea may very well bury the idea.

I start out in the first chapter with certain axioms—statements which are taken for granted—and try to lead the student to derive other statements as *necessary consequences* of the axioms. From the axioms and from these new statements—true in the sense that they are consequences of the axioms—still other and perhaps deeper statements may be derived. In this way a kind of structure of ideas may be built up. Suppose, now, that the student is unable to supply an argument to establish the truth of some statement upon which further developments depend. Rather than seek help from someone or from some other book, he should take this unsettled thing for granted temporarily and go on to further developments. With additional experience he may be able later on to go back and fill in the gap. As long as the question remains unsettled, he continues to have a nice problem to work on, and if he has been able to assimilate the creative spirit which this book attempts to instill, he will regard an unsolved problem not as a frustration but as a challenge!

This book is designed to give the student an opportunity to prove theorems for himself. A *proof* of a theorem consists of a suitable succession of statements each of which is completely justified. It has been my experience that there will be about as many different proofs of certain theorems as there are students who have proved them in my classes. I would not say that one of these proofs is *better* than another. Different people think in different ways and each should be encouraged to think in his own way. It is thus that new ideas are born!

This book is the outgrowth of the ideas and inspiration of my many students over the years and I wish to express to them my thanks and my feelings of admiration. I wish to thank, in particular, Mr. Michael Steib who made the drawings. Thanks are due the staff of the University of Texas Press for their many kindnesses.

H. S. W.

CONTENTS

CREATIVE MATHEMATICS

Mathematics is a creation of the mind. To begin with, there is a collection of things, which exist only in the mind, assumed to be distinguishable from one another; and then there is a collection of statements about these things, which are taken for granted. Starting with the assumed statements concerning these invented or imagined things, the mathematician discovers other statements, called theorems, and proves them as necessary consequences. This, in brief, is the pattern of mathematics. The mathematician is an artist whose medium is the mind and whose creations are ideas.

Numbers

We assume the existence of certain things called *numbers*, some of which are called *counting numbers*, and we take for granted certain statements concerning numbers, called *axioms*. The first few axioms are as follows.

Axiom I
If x is a number and y a number, then $x + y$ (read x *plus* y) is a number called the *sum* of x and y. The association with x and y of the sum $x + y$ is called *addition*.

Axiom II
If each of x, y, and z is a number, then $x + (y + z)$ is $(x + y) + z$.

Axiom III
0 is a number such that, if x is a number, $0 + x$ is x.

Axiom IV
If x is a number, then $-x$ is a number such that $x + (-x)$ is 0.

Axiom V
If x and y are numbers, then $x + y$ is $y + x$.

A suitable question may lead to a theorem and one question may lead to another. For example, a study of Axiom III could suggest the question: Is 0 the *only* number with the property that, if x is a number, $0 + x$ is x? It may be shown on the basis of Axiom's III and V that the answer to this question is in the affirmative, so that we have:

Theorem A. If $0'$ (read 0 *prime*) is a number such that, if x is a number, $0' + x$ is x, then $0'$ is 0.

We suggest that the reader try to construct an argument to prove this theorem on the basis of the above axioms. He may then want to compare his argument with that given in the sample proofs at the end of the present chapter.

The number 0—such that, if x is a number, $0 + x$ is x—is called *zero*.

Can Theorem A be improved upon by requiring *less* of the number $0'$ in order to have, as a consequence, $0'$ is 0? Such a result is Theorem A' at the end of the chapter. Before reading further, it is suggested that the student try to discover and prove some more theorems for himself.

Theorem B. If x is a number and y a number such that $x + y$ is 0, then y is -x.

If x is a number, *the* number -x—such that $x + (-x)$ is 0—is called *minus x* or *the negative* of x. If y is a number and x a number, the number $y + (-x)$ may be denoted by $y - x$. This is called the *difference y minus x* or simply y *minus* x. The association with y and x of the difference $y - x$ is called *subtraction*.

Theorem C. If y is a number and z a number, the only number x such that $y + x$ is z is the number $z - y$. (That is, $z - y$ *is a number x such that $y + x$ is z; and, if x is a number such that $y + x$ is z, then x is $z - y$*).

Theorem D. If x is a number, then $-(-x)$ is x.

Theorem E. -0 is 0.

The next few axioms are as follows.

Axiom VI
If x is a number and y a number, then $x \cdot y$ (read x *times* y) is a number called the *product* of x and y. The association with x and y of the product $x \cdot y$ is called *multiplication*.

Axiom VII
If each of x, y, and z is a number, then $x \cdot (y \cdot z)$ is $(x \cdot y) \cdot z$.

Axiom VIII
1 is a number such that, if x is a number, $1 \cdot x$ is x.

Axiom IX
If x is a number distinct from 0, then $1/x$ is a number such that $x \cdot (1/x)$ is 1.

Axiom X
If x and y are numbers, then $x \cdot y$ is $y \cdot x$.

Axiom XI
The number 0 is not the number 1.

Axiom XII
If each of x, y, and z is a number, then $x \cdot (y + z)$ is $(x \cdot y) + (x \cdot z)$.

For the sake of simplicity, the last number, $(x \cdot y) + (x \cdot z)$, may be written without the parentheses: $x \cdot y + x \cdot z$.

The Axioms VI, VII, VIII, IX and X resemble the Axioms I, II, III, IV and V, respectively. There is one important difference: the proviso *distinct from* 0 in Axiom IX has no counterpart in Axiom IV.

Exercise. Discover and prove theorems concerning multiplication, lettered a, a′, b, c, d, and e, which are analogous to theorems A, A′, B, C, D, and E, respectively, concerning addition.

The number 1—such that, if x is a number, $1 \cdot x$ is x—is called *one*. If x is a number distinct from 0, *the* number $1/x$ of Axiom IX is called the *reciprocal* of x. If z is a number and y a number distinct from 0, *the* number x, such that $y \cdot x$ is z, namely $z \cdot (1/y)$, is denoted by z/y and called the *quotient z over y*. The association with z and y of the quotient z/y is called *division*.

Theorem F. If x is a number, $0 \cdot x$ is 0.

Theorem G. If x is a number and y a number and $x \cdot y$ is 0, then x is 0 or y is 0 (*i.e.*, if x is not 0, then y is 0).

Theorem H. If x is a number, $-1 \cdot x$ is $-x$.

Theorem J. If x is a number and y a number, then $(-x) \cdot (-y)$ is $x \cdot y$.

Note that the meaning of the word *or* is established in Theorem G. The meaning of the word *only* is established in Theorem C.

It is an interesting puzzle to prove Theorem F without the use of Axiom IV, *i.e.*, without the use of negatives of numbers.

The remaining axioms involve the symbol $<$ (read *is less than*). It is convenient to use the symbol $=$ to mean is. Thus, if x is a number and y a number, $x = y$ means x is y, $x < y$ is read x *is less than* y and the denials may be expressed by : $x \neq y$, x *is not* y or x *is distinct from* y, and $x \not< y$, x *is not less than* y.

If x and y are numbers, the statement $x > y$ means $y < x$ and is read x *is greater than* y or x *exceeds* y. The statement that $x \not> y$

means *x is not greater than y*, *i.e.*, $x = y$ or $x < y$. The statement that *x is positive* means $x > 0$ and the statement *x is negative* means $x < 0$.

Axiom XIII
If x and y are numbers, then $x < y$ or $y < x$.

Axiom XIV
If each of x, y, and z is a number and $x < y$, then $x + z < y + z$.

Axiom XV
If each of x, y, and z is a number, $x < y$ and $0 < z$, then $z \cdot x < z \cdot y$.

Axiom XVI
If each of x, y, and z is a number, $x < y$ and $y < z$, then $x < z$.

The next axiom tells the distinguishing things about the *counting numbers*, mentioned in the first sentence of this chapter.

Axiom XVII
The number 1 is a counting number and, if x is a number such that $x < 1$, then x is not a counting number; if x is a counting number, then $x + 1$ is a counting number and, if z is a number such that $x < z$ and $z < x + 1$, then z is not a counting number.

Axiom XVIII
If M is a set each element of which is a number and if there is a number which is less than no number of M, then there is a number k which is less than no number of M such that, if k' is a number less than k, then k' is less than *some* number of M. The number k is called *the least number which no number in* M *exceeds*.

This completes our list of axioms.

Exercise. Show that each of the following statements is a theorem.
    (i) If x is a number and y a number, then only one of the following statements is true:
$$x = y, \qquad x < y, \qquad y < x.$$
  (ii) $0 < 1$.
  (iii) If x is a number and $0 < x$, then $0 < (1/x)$.
  (iv) If x and y are numbers, $0 < x$ and $x < y$, then $(1/y) < (1/x)$.
  (v) If x and y are numbers and $y < x$, then there exists a number k such that $0 < k$ and $y + k = x$.
  (vi) If x is a number, then $x < x + 1$.
  (vii) If each of x, y, u, and v is a number, $x < y$ and $u < v$, then $x + u < y + v$.
  (viii) If x and y are numbers and $x < y$, then $-y < -x$.

The statement that the number y is *between* the number x and the number z means that $x < y$ and $y < z$ or $z < y$ and $y < x$. If y is between x and z then y is between z and $\overline{x}$.

Theorem. Suppose each of x, y, and z is a number. The following statements are equivalent:
(i) y is between x and z, and
(ii) there exists a number t between 0 and 1 such that $y = t \cdot x + (1 - t) \cdot z$.

Note. This means that, if (i) is true, then (ii) is true *and*, if (ii) is true, then (i) is true. Thus, either statement may be substituted for the other in any argument.

Problem. Suppose each of p and q is a positive number. Find (i) a number which is greater than both p and q and (ii) a positive number which is less than both p and q, *i.e.*, a number which is between 0 and q *and* between 0 and p.

Theorem. If M is a set each element of which is a number and there is a number which exceeds no number of M, then there is a number h which exceeds no number of M and, if h' is a number greater than h, then h' exceeds *some* number of M.

The number h of this theorem is called *the largest number which exceeds no number of M*.

A set each element of which is a number is called a *number set*. A number set containing only one number is a different thing from this number.

The largest number which exceeds no positive number is not in the set of positive numbers.

Theorem. If M is a number set and each number in M is a counting number, then the largest number which exceeds no number of M *belongs to the set* M, *i.e.*, M contains a number which is less than any other number of M.

Exercise. Show that each of the following statements is a theorem.
(i) If x is a number, there do not exist counting numbers m and n both of which are between x and $x + 1$.
(ii) If h is a number greater than 1 which is not a counting number, then there exists a counting number n such that h is between n and $n + 1$.
(iii) If n is a counting number greater than 1, then $n - 1$ is a counting number.

(iv) If m is a counting number and n a counting number, then $m + n$ is a counting number and $m \cdot n$ is a counting number.

(v) If d is a positive number and k a positive number, then there exists a counting number n such that $n \cdot d > k$.

Suppose x is a number. The statement that x is a *positive integer* means that x is a counting number; the statement that x is a *negative integer* means that x is the negative of a counting number; the statement that x is an *integer* means that x is a negative integer, x is 0, or x is a positive integer; and the statement that x is a *rational number* means that there exists an integer m and an integer n such that x is the quotient m/n.

Exercise. Show that each of the following statements is a theorem.

(i) If x and y are numbers, there is a rational number between x and y.

(ii) If M is a number set containing 1 such that, if x belongs to M then $x + 1$ belongs to M, then every counting number belongs to M. Thus, the set of counting numbers consists of $1, 1 + 1$ or $2, 2 + 1$ or 3, $3 + 1$ or 4, and so forth.

(iii) If each of x and y is a number, $-x \cdot y = -(x \cdot y)$.

(iv) If each of x and y is a number, $-(x + y) = -x - y$.

(v) If x is a number, $x/1 = x$.

(vi) If each of x, y, u, and v is a number, and $u \neq 0$ and $v \neq 0$, then

$$\frac{x}{u} \cdot \frac{y}{v} = \frac{x \cdot y}{u \cdot v} \quad .$$

(vii) If x is a number and y a number distinct from 0, then

$$-\frac{x}{y} = \frac{-x}{y} = \frac{x}{-y} \quad .$$

(viii) If each of a, b, c, and d is a number, and $c \neq 0$ and $d \neq 0$, then

$$\frac{a}{c} + \frac{b}{d} = \frac{a \cdot d + b \cdot c}{c \cdot d}$$

If a is a number and b a number, the product $a \cdot b$ may be written as ab, with the dot omitted. Also, the product aa is denoted by a^2, aa^2 by a^3, aa^3 by a^4, and so forth. The number a^2 is read a *squared*, a^3 is read a *cubed*, a^4 is read a *to the fourth power*.

(ix) If each of a and b is a number, then $(a + b)(a - b) = a^2 - b^2$ and $(a + b)^2 = a^2 + 2ab + b^2$. (Here, $2ab$ means $ab + ab$).

(x) If a is a number and b a number, then $a^2 + 2ab + b^2 > 0$ unless $a = -b$.

Theorem. If a is a positive number, there exists a positive number x such that $x^2 = a$.

A straight line drawn on a writing surface, imagined of indefinite extent, serves as a model for the numbers. Suppose the line is drawn horizontally and extends indefinitely to the right and to the left. A dot on the line is selected and identified with the number 0. Each dot on the line is supposed to be identified with a number and each number with a dot on the line in such a way that, if x and y are numbers and $x < y$, then the dot identified with x is to the left of the dot identified with y; and if X and Y are numbers and Y - X $= y - x$, then the piece of the line with ends identified with x and y is commensurate with the piece of the line with ends identified with X and Y.

```
-5   -4   -3   -2   -1    0    1    2    3    4    5
 •    •    •    •    •    •    •    •    •    •    •
```

We borrow from this model the notions: *interval* and *length* of an interval. The statement that $[a,b]$ is an interval means that a and b are numbers, $a < b$ and $[a,b]$ is the number set to which x belongs only if x is a, x is b, or x is a number between a and b. The length of the interval $[a,b]$ is the positive number $b - a$.

SAMPLE PROOFS

Theorem A. If 0' is a number such that, if x is a number, 0' $+ x$ is x, then 0' is 0.

Proof. Suppose 0' is a number such that, if x is a number, 0' $+x$ is x. Then, since 0 is a number, by Axiom III,

$$0' + 0 \text{ is } 0$$

and, since 0' $+ 0$ is $0 + 0'$, by Axiom V:

$$0 + 0' \text{ is } 0.$$

But, since 0' is a number, by hypothesis, it follows from Axiom III that $0 + 0'$ is 0', so that 0' is 0, as was to be proved.

Theorem C. If y is a number and z a number, the only number x such that $y + x$ is z is the number $z - y$.

11

Proof.   Suppose, first, that y is a number and z a number and that x is a number such that $y + x$ is z.   Then:

$$x + y \text{ is } z \qquad \text{(Axiom V)}$$
$$(x + y) + (-y) \text{ is } z + (-y) \qquad \text{(Axioms IV and I)}$$
$$x + [y + (-y)] \text{ is } z + (-y) \qquad \text{(Axiom II)}$$
$$x + 0 \text{ is } z + (-y) \qquad \text{(Axiom IV)}$$
$$0 + x \text{ is } z + (-y) \qquad \text{(Axiom V)}$$
$$x \text{ is } z + (-y) \qquad \text{(Axiom III)}$$

i.e., x is $z - y$.   Thus, *if* there is a number x such that $y + x$ is z, *then* x is $z - y$.

It remains to be shown that, if x is $z - y$, then $y + x$ is z.   We have

$$x \text{ is } z - y \qquad \text{(Given)}$$
$$y + x \text{ is } y + [z - y] \qquad \text{(Axiom I)}$$
$$y + x \text{ is } y + [(-y) + z] \qquad \text{(Axiom V)}$$
$$y + x \text{ is } [y + (-y)] + z \qquad \text{(Axiom II)}$$
$$y + x \text{ is } 0 + z \qquad \text{(Axiom IV)}$$
$$y + x \text{ is } z \qquad \text{(Axiom III)},$$

as was to be proved.

Note.   *Only x* means *x and no other*.   Theorem C states that *the* number $z - y$, and *no other* number, has a certain property.

Theorem.   If m is a counting number and n a counting number then $m + n$ is a counting number.

Proof.   Suppose m is a counting number.   Then, by Axiom XVII, $m + 1$ is a counting number.   Suppose there is a counting number n such that $m + n$ is *not* a counting number and denote by M the set to which x belongs only if x is a counting number such that $m + x$ is not a counting number.   Since 1 is not in M and, by Axiom XVII, no counting number is less than 1, then each number in M is greater than 1 (Axiom XIII).   By an earlier theorem, there is a number k in M which is less than any other number of M.   Since k is a counting number greater than 1, then $k - 1$ is a counting number (by an earlier theorem).   Now,

$$m + k = [m + (k - 1)] + 1 \qquad \text{(Axioms II, V, III)}.$$

Since $k - 1$ is a counting number, *not in* M, then $m + (k - 1)$ is a counting number, and $[m + (k - 1)] + 1$ is therefore a counting number by Axiom XVII, *i.e.*, $m + k$ is a counting number.   This is a contradiction of the fact that k is in M.   Thus, the set M does not exist—there is no number n such that $m + n$ is not a counting number.   This establishes the theorem.

Theorem A'.   If $0'$ is a number such that, for *some* number x, $0' + x$ is x, then $0'$ is 0.

Ordered Number Pairs

The statement that P is a *point* means that P is an ordered number pair (x,y) having a first number x called the *abscissa* of P and a second number y called the *ordinate* of P. A *point set* is a collection each element of which is a point.

A plane writing surface, *e.g.*, a blackboard, imagined of indefinite extent, may serve as a model for the set of all points. From the set of all horizontal lines on the surface select one and designate it $\underline{0}$ (read 0-*horizontal*) and from the set of all vertical lines on the surface select one and designate it $0|$ (read 0-*vertical*). Regard each of these as a model for the set of all numbers, as described near the end of the preceding chapter, 0 being at the intersection, the positive numbers to the right on $\underline{0}$ and the positive numbers upward on $0|$. If x is a number on $\underline{0}$, denote by $x|$ (read x-*vertical*), the straight line containing x which is vertical, and, if y is a number on $0|$, denote by $\underline{y}$ (read y-*horizontal*), the straight line containing y which is horizontal. The point (x,y) is identified with the intersection of $x|$ and $\underline{y}$ (See figure).

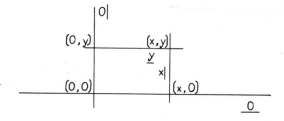

In the preceding discussion, *straight line* means a kind of mark on a writing surface—a physical thing. We may now define horizontal and vertical lines as point sets: the statement that y is a horizontal line means $\underline{y}$ is the set of all points with ordinate the number y and the statement that $x|$ is a vertical line means $x|$ is the set of all points with abscissa the number x.

We borrow from the model for the set of all points the notions: *rectangular interval* and *area* of a rectangular interval. The statement that $[ab;cd]$ is a rectangular interval means $[a,b]$ is an interval, $[c,d]$ is an interval and $[ab;cd]$ is the point set to which (x,y) belongs only if x belongs to $[a,b]$ and y to $[c,d]$.

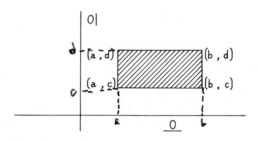

The area of the rectangular interval $[ab;cd]$ is the positive number $(b - a) \cdot (d - c)$.

A point set f such that no two points of f have the same abscissa is called a *simple graph*. For instance, a point set containing only one point is a simple graph; a horizontal line is a simple graph.

THE SIMPLE GRAPH L

We denote by H the simple graph to which the point (x,y) belongs only if x is a positive number and y is the reciprocal of x. The accompanying figure shows a picture of H. It consists of all the points $(x, (1/x))$ for which $x > 0$.

If P and Q are points of H and P is to the left of Q, then P is *higher* than Q.

In the accompanying figure, x is a number greater than 1 so that the point $(x,0)$ is to the right of the point $(1,0)$. The point set S represented by the shaded region may be described as follows: S is the point set to which the point (u,v) belongs only if u belongs to the interval $[1,x]$ and v is 0, v is $1/u$ or v is a number between 0 and $1/u$.

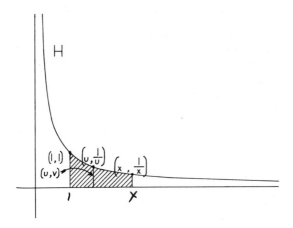

Question. We have defined the area of the rectangular interval $[ab;cd]$ to be the number $(b - a)(d - c)$. How shall we define a number suitable to be called the area of the point set S? What would we mean by the area of a field shaped like the shaded region in the figure?

One way to allow the reader more time to try to arrive at a definition of area of the region S is to bypass the question temporarily and *assume* that there is a number suitable to be called the area of the region S. In order to discuss this number, it is convenient to introduce the following definition: the statement that $[H;a,b]$ is the region determined by H and the interval $[a,b]$ means that $[a,b]$ is an interval of positive numbers and $[H;a,b]$ is the point set to which (x,y) belongs only if x belongs to $[a,b]$ and y to $[0, (1/x)]$. In this notation, the shaded region S of the preceding figure is $[H;1,x]$. We assume that the *area* of the region $[H;a,b]$ determined by H and the interval $[a,b]$ is a positive number, denoted by $\int_a^b H$, having the following properties:

(i)
$$(b - a) \cdot \frac{1}{b} < \int_a^b H < (b - a) \cdot \frac{1}{a}$$

and

(ii) if c is a number between a and b,
$$\int_a^b H = \int_a^c H + \int_c^b H.$$

15

Condition (i) states that the area $\int_a^b H$ of $[H;a,b]$ is a number between the area of the rectangular interval $[ab;0(1/b)]$ and the area of the rectangular interval $[ab;0(1/a)]$, the first included in $[H;a,b]$ and the second including $[H;a,b]$; and condition (ii) states that, if c is a number between a and b, then the area of $[H;a,b]$ is the sum of the area of $[H;a,c]$ and the area of $[H;c,b]$ (See figure).

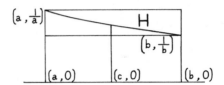

If p and q are numbers and $p < q$, the number $(1/2)[p+q]$ is a number r called the *average* of p and q which has the property of being between p and q and also the property that $r - p = q - r$, i.e., the length of $[p,r]$ is the length of $[r,q]$. Thus, the number r *bisects* the interval $[p,q]$. If x is a number between p and q, then x differs from this number r by less than $(1/2)(q - p)$, i.e., by less than one-half the length of $[p,q]$. *It follows that* $\int_a^b H$ *differs from the average of* $(b - a) \cdot (1/b)$ *and* $(b - a) \cdot (1/a)$ *by less than* $\dfrac{(b - a)^2}{2ab}$. Thus,

$$\int_a^b H \text{ is approximately } \frac{b^2 - a^2}{2ab}, \text{ with error } < \frac{(b - a)^2}{2ab}.$$

If, for example, a is not less than 1 and $b - a = .1$, then the error in the approximation is less than .005, so that the ''approximate formula'' is accurate to two decimal places.

Example. $\quad \displaystyle\int_1^{1.1} H = \frac{(1.1)^2 - 1^2}{2.2} = .095,$

$$\int_{1.1}^{1.2} H = \frac{(1.2)^2 - (1.1)^2}{(2.2)(1.2)} = .087.$$

Then, by (ii),

$$\int_1^{1.2} H = \int_1^{1.1} H + \int_{1.1}^{1.2} H = .182.$$

These approximations are accurate to about two decimal places.

Exercise.   Complete the following table of approximations.

x	$\int_1^x H$
1.1	.095
1.2	.182
1.3	
1.4	
1.5	
1.6	
1.7	
1.8	
1.9	
2.0	

Definition.   L denotes the simple graph to which the point (x,y) belongs only if x is a positive number and

$$y = \begin{cases} -\int_x^1 H, & \text{if } 0 < x < 1, \\ 0, & \text{if } x = 1, \\ \int_1^x H, & \text{if } 1 < x. \end{cases}$$

Problems.

1. Find any evidence you can to support the following statement: If x is a number greater than 1, then

$$\int_{1/x}^1 H = \int_1^x H.$$

17

2. Find any evidence you can to support the following statement: If c is a positive number, then the area of $[H;a,b]$ is the area of $[H;ca,cb]$, i.e.,

$$\int_a^b H = \int_{ca}^{cb} H, \qquad \text{if } 0 < a < b \text{ and } 0 < c.$$

3. Use the computations of the last Exercise and the statement in Problem 1 to draw a sketch of the simple graph L.

Definition. If f is a simple graph, the ordinate of that point of f whose abscissa is the number x is denoted by $f(x)$ (read f of x).

For example, if x is a positive number, $H(x) = 1/x$. Also, $L(1) = 0$, $L(1.1) = .095$, $L(1.2) = .182$, the last two only approximately, and, if x is a positive number,

$$L(x) = \begin{cases} -\int_x^1 H, & \text{if } 0 < x < 1, \\ 0, & \text{if } x = 1, \\ \int_1^x H, & \text{if } 1 < x. \end{cases}$$

Exercise. Assume the properties of area of $[H;a,b]$ and the statements in Problems 1 and 2, above, to prove the following statements:

(i) $\int_a^b H = L(b) - L(a)$,   if $0 < a < b$,

(ii) $L(b) - L(a) = L(ca) - L(cb)$,   if $0 < a < b$ and $0 < c$,

(iii) if each of x and y is a positive number, then

$$L(xy) = L(x) + L(y),$$

$$L(x/y) = L(x) - L(y),$$

$$\text{and } L(1/x) = -L(x).$$

Use these formulas and computations already made to find approximations to $L(3)$, $L(5)$, $L(7)$, $L(11)$, $L(13)$, $L(17)$, $L(19)$. For example, knowing approximations to $L(1.5)$, which is $L(3/2)$ or $L(3) - L(2)$, and $L(2)$, an approximation to $L(3)$ can be obtained. Next, use these results to find approximations to $L(.1)$, $L(.2)$, $L(.3)$, $L(.4)$, $L(.5)$, $L(.6)$, $L(.7)$, $L(.8)$ and $L(.9)$.

The problem of *defining* the area of $[H;a,b]$ involves picking out a certain number from the set of all numbers. The axiom preeminently adapted to this purpose is Axiom XVIII. First, we try to define a number set M no number of which exceeds some number k and such that the *least* such number k not exceeded by any number of M has the properties required of the number we are trying to define. The "geometry" could lead to an idea for setting up the number set M. For the present we shall continue to assume that $[\mathrm{H};a,b]$ has an area with the properties already specified, and that the statements made in Problems 1 and 2, above, are true. We then have the formulas of the last Exercise at our disposal.

THE LOGARITHM

If a is a positive number distinct from 1 and x a positive number, *the logarithm of x to the base a*, denoted by $\log_a x$, is the number $\dfrac{\mathrm{L}(x)}{\mathrm{L}(a)}$:

$$\log_a x = \frac{\mathrm{L}(x)}{\mathrm{L}(a)}.$$

The logarithm to the base 10 is called the *common logarithm.* Thus, $\log_{10} 2 = \dfrac{\mathrm{L}(2)}{\mathrm{L}(10)} = .301$. Common logarithms are used to reduce the problems of multiplication and division to the simpler problems of addition and subtraction. Tables have been computed for this purpose. Also, the slide rule furnishes a mechanical means to the same end.

Exercise. Show that, if each of x and y is a positive number and each of a and b a positive number distinct from 1, then

$$\log_a xy = \log_a x + \log_a y,$$

$$\log_a \frac{x}{y} = \log_a x - \log_a y,$$

and
$$\log_a \frac{1}{x} = -\log_a x.$$

Moreover, $(\log_a b)(\log_b a) = 1$. Show that, if n is an integer,

$$\log_{10}(10^n x) = n + \log_{10} x.$$

For instance, $\log_{10} 20 = 1.301$, and $\log_{10} .2 = .301 - 1$. Here, 10^{-1} means .1, 10^{-2} means .01, etc.

The statement that S is an inner sum for the region $[\mathrm{H};a,b]$ means there exists a finite collection G of nonoverlapping intervals filling up

$[a,b]$ such that, if the length of each interval $[p,q]$ in G is multiplied by $1/q$, then the sum of all the products so formed is S.

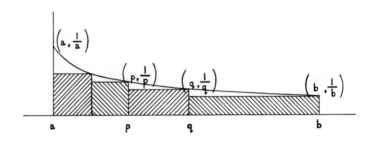

An inner sum for $[H;a,b]$ is the sum of the areas of one or more rectangular intervals. The simplest is $(b - a) \cdot (1/b)$. The next simplest is the sum of the areas of two rectangular intervals: $(c - a) \cdot (1/c) + (b - c) \cdot (1/b)$, where $a < c < b$. The inner sum corresponding to the figure shown above is the sum of the areas of five rectangular intervals.

Every inner sum for $[H;a,b]$ *is less than* $(b - a) \cdot (1/a)$. Hence, by Axiom XVIII, there is a least number k which no inner sum for $[H;a,b]$ exceeds. This number k is taken as the area of $[H;a,b]$ and denoted by the symbol $\int_a^b H$ (read: the area of the region determined by H and $[a,b]$).

Theorem. Suppose a and b are positive numbers, $a < b$ and c is a positive number. The following statements are true:

(i) $(b - a) \cdot \dfrac{1}{b} < \int_a^b H < (b - a) \cdot \dfrac{1}{a}$.

(ii) If c is between a and b, $\int_a^b H = \int_a^c H + \int_c^b H$.

(iii) $\int_a^b H = \int_{ca}^{cb} H$.

The establishment of this theorem will give substance to this chapter, based up to now upon conjecture.

In a proof of (ii), it may be useful to turn to our straight line model for the numbers. If $x = \int_a^c H$, $y = \int_c^b H$, and $z = \int_a^b H$, then only one of the following statements is true:

$$z < x + y, \qquad z > x + y, \qquad \text{or} \qquad z = x + y.$$

If the first two statements can be proved impossible, then the last is true, *i.e.*, (ii) is true. The first two statements may be pictured as shown:

No inner sum for $[H;a,c]$ exceeds x but, if x' is a number less than x, *some* inner sum for $[H;a, c]$ exceeds x'; a similar statement holds for y and z.

PROPERTIES OF L

We state here some properties of the simple graph L which may be proved on the basis of properties already discovered, *e.g.*,

$$L(b) - L(a) = \int_a^b H, \qquad\qquad \text{if } 0 < a < b,$$

$$(b - a) \cdot \frac{1}{b} < \int_a^b H < (b - a) \cdot \frac{1}{a},$$

and
$$L(xy) = L(x) + L(y), \qquad\qquad \text{if } x > 0,\, y > 0.$$

i. If h is a number, there exists a point of L above the horizontal line h and a point of L below the horizontal line h.

ii. If x and y are positive numbers and $x < y$, then $L(x) < L(y)$.

iii. If h is a number, the horizontal line h contains a point of L but does not contain two points of L.

Definition. The X-projection of the simple graph f is the number set to which x belongs only if x is the abscissa of a point of f. The Y-projection of the simple graph f is the number set to which y belongs only if y is the ordinate of a point of f.

The X-projection of L is, by definition of L, the set of all *positive* numbers. Statement No. iii, above, shows that *the* Y-*projection of L is the set of all numbers*.

THE SIMPLE GRAPH E

The point set to which (x,y) belongs only if (y,x) belongs to L is a simple graph, which we denote by E. The X-projection of E is the set of all numbers and the Y-projection of E is the set of all positive numbers. The accompanying figure shows a sketch of L and of E.

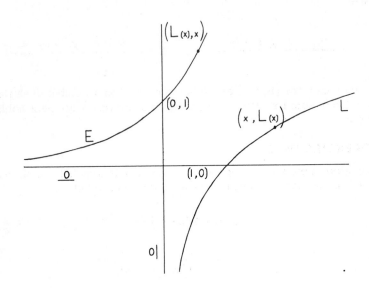

From the definition of E and properties of L, the reader may establish the following properties of E.

    i. If x and y are numbers and $x < y$, then $E(x) < E(y)$.

    ii. If x is a number, $L\{E(x)\} = x$ and, if x is a positive number, $E\{L(x)\} = x$.

    iii. If x is a number and c a number, then

$$E(x + c) = E(x) \cdot E(c).$$

    iv. If e denotes the number $E(1)$, then $L(e) = 1$, and $2.7 < e < 2.8$.

    v. $E(1) = e$, $E(2) = e^2$, $E(3) = e^3$, and, if n is a positive integer, $E(n) = e^n$.

    vi. If x is a number, $E(-x) = \dfrac{1}{E(x)}$.

POWERS AND ROOTS

    Definition. If a is a positive number and x a number, then a^x (read *a to the x*) is the number $E\{x L(a)\}$:

$$a^x = E\{x L(a)\}.$$

In particular, $e^x = E(x)$.

Examples. If a is a positive number, $a^0 = 1$ and $a^1 = a$ and, if n is a positive integer, $a^n = a \cdot a^{n-1}$. If x is a number, $1^x = 1$.

Theorem. If each of a and b is a positive number and each of x and y is a number, then the following statements are true.

(i) $a^x a^y = a^{x+y}$,

(ii) $(a^x)^y = a^{xy}$,

(iii) $a^x b^x = (ab)^x$,

(iv) $a^{-x} = \dfrac{1}{(a^x)}$,

(v) $\dfrac{a^x}{a^y} = a^{x-y}$,

(vi) $\dfrac{a^x}{b^x} = \left(\dfrac{a}{b}\right)^x$,

(vii) $L(a^x) = x L(a)$,

(viii) $\log_b a^x = x \cdot \log_b a$,

(ix) if n is a positive integer,

$$(a^{1/n})^n = a.$$

Definitions. The number $a^{1/2}$ is called the positive square root of the positive number a and may be denoted by $\sqrt{a}$. This is the only positive number whose square is a. If n is an integer greater than 2, $a^{1/n}$ is called the positive nth root of a and may be denoted by $\sqrt[n]{a}$.

THE SIMPLE GRAPH Q

Q denotes the simple graph whose X-projection is the set of all nonnegative numbers defined as follows:

$$Q(x) = \begin{cases} 0, & \text{if } x = 0, \\ x^{1/2}, & \text{if } x > 0. \end{cases}$$

The accompanying figure shows a sketch of the simple graph Q.

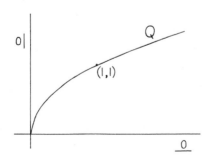

Q

$(1,1)$

0

0

Definition. If x is a number, $|x|$ (read *the absolute value of x*) is the number $Q(x^2)$.

Exercise. Show that if x is a number and y a number, then

$$|x + y| \not> |x| + |y|,$$

i.e., $|x + y|$ is less than or equal to $|x| + |y|$. This may be written $|x + y| \leq |x| + |y|$.

Slope

STRAIGHT LINES

The statement that f is the straight line of *slope* m containing the point (a,b) means that m is a number and f the simple graph such that, for every number x,

$$f(x) = m \cdot (x - a) + b.$$

Exercise

(i) Show that, if (x,y) and (u,v) are points of the straight line of slope m containing the point (a,b), then

$$m = \frac{y - v}{x - u}.$$

(ii) Sketch the straight line of slope 1 containing the point $(0,0)$ and the straight line of slope -1 containing the point $(0,0)$.

(iii) Suppose c is a positive number. Determine a number m such that the straight line of slope m containing the point $(c, L(c))$ has none of its points below L.

(iv) Suppose c is a positive number. Show that the straight line of slope $-(1/c)^2$ containing the point $(c, (1/c))$ has none of its points above H.

(v) Suppose W is the simple graph such that, if x is a number, $W(x) = x^2$. If c is a number, determine a number m such that the straight line of slope m containing (c, c^2) has none of its points above W.

(vi) Suppose P and Q are points of a straight line of slope m. Show that, if P is to the left of Q, then P is lower than Q or P is higher than Q according as $m > 0$ or $m < 0$, respectively.

COMPUTATION FORMULAS FOR L

It is possible to *conjecture* formulas for computation of $L(c)$ from geometrical considerations. We suppose $c > 1$. Inasmuch as $(c - 1) \cdot (1/c)$, i.e., $(c - 1)/c$, is an inner sum for $[H;1,c]$, it follows that $L(c) > (c - 1)/c$, so that there exists a positive number k_1 such that

$$L(c) = \frac{c - 1}{c} + k_1, \qquad 0 < k_1.$$

To obtain a number larger than k_1, we see from the accompanying

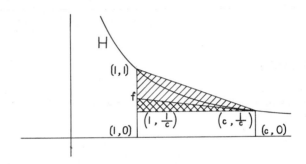

figure that k_1 appears to be less than the area

$$\frac{1}{2}(c - 1)\left(1 - \frac{1}{c}\right) \text{ or } \frac{1}{2}\left(\frac{c - 1}{c}\right)^2 \cdot c.$$

of the shaded triangular region. Thus,

$$L(c) = \frac{c - 1}{c} + k_1, \quad 0 < k_1 < \frac{1}{2}\left(\frac{c - 1}{c}\right)^2 \cdot c$$

To obtain a second approximation to $L(c)$, we make use of (iv) of the last exercise. The straight line f containing the point $(c,(1/c))$ of slope $-(1/c)^2$, defined for every number x by

$$f(x) = -\left(\frac{1}{c}\right)^2 (x - c) + \frac{1}{c},$$

has none of its points above H (See figure). Hence, $L(c)$ is less than $(c - 1)/c$ plus the area of the shaded smaller triangular region; *i.e.*,

$$L(c) = \frac{c - 1}{c} + \frac{1}{2}\left(\frac{c - 1}{c}\right)^2 + k_2, \qquad 0 < k_2.$$

26

By analogy with the first approximation formula, we *conjecture* that $k_2 < \frac{1}{3}\left(\frac{c-1}{c}\right)^3 \cdot c$; *i.e.*,

$$L(c) = \frac{c-1}{c} + \frac{1}{2}\left(\frac{c-1}{c}\right)^2 + k_2, \qquad 0 < k_2 < \frac{1}{3}\left(\frac{c-1}{c}\right)^3 \cdot c$$

Having gone this far, we now *conjecture*

$$L(c) = \frac{c-1}{c} + \frac{1}{2}\left(\frac{c-1}{c}\right)^2 + \frac{1}{3}\left(\frac{c-1}{c}\right)^3 + k_3, \qquad 0 < k_3 < \frac{1}{4}\left(\frac{c-1}{c}\right)^4 \cdot c$$

and so on.

It is evident that, if our formulas are correct, they give better approximations the nearer c is to 1. To obtain experimental evidence in support of our conjectured formulas, we note that $L(2)$, $L(3)$, $L(5)$, and $L(7)$ can be found from $L\left(\frac{25}{24}\right)$, $L\left(\frac{36}{35}\right)$, $L\left(\frac{81}{80}\right)$, and $L\left(\frac{225}{224}\right)$ or by means of other fractions greater than 1 involving only the integers 2, 3, 5, and 7 as factors. In fact,

$$L\left(\frac{25}{24}\right) = -3L(2) - L(3) + 2L(5),$$

$$L\left(\frac{36}{35}\right) = 2L(2) + 2L(3) - L(5) - L(7),$$

$$L\left(\frac{81}{80}\right) = -4L(2) + 4L(3) - L(5),$$

$$L\left(\frac{225}{224}\right) = -5L(2) + 2L(3) + 2L(5) - L(7).$$

Now, if $c = \frac{25}{24}$, so that $\frac{c-1}{c} = \frac{1}{25} = .04$, then we find by means of the fourth formula;

$$L\left(\frac{25}{24}\right) = .04 + .0008 + .000021333 + .00000064 + k_4,$$

where $0 < k_4 < .000000021$, so that $L\left(\frac{25}{24}\right) = .0408220$, is correct to 7 decimal places. Likewise;

$$L\left(\frac{36}{35}\right) = .0281709, \quad L\left(\frac{81}{80}\right) = .0124225, \quad L\left(\frac{225}{224}\right) = .0044543.$$

We then find the values,

L(2) = .69315, L(3) = 1.09861, L(5) = 1.60944, L(7) = 1.94591. Now, $\log_{10} 2 = \dfrac{L(2)}{L(10)} = .30103$, from these computed values. This agrees with the value of the common logarithm of 2 in a five place table. Other checks may be devised. For instance, from our computation formulas we get $L\left(\dfrac{10}{9}\right) = .10536$ and, from the above values, $L\left(\dfrac{10}{9}\right)$ = L(2) + L(5) - 2L(3) = .10536.

The experimental evidence tends to support our formulas.

COMPUTATION OF e

The number E(1), denoted by e, is the number x such that $L(x) = 1$. Inasmuch as L(2) = .69315 and L(3) = 1.09861, we see that $2 < e < 3$ and e is nearer to 3 than to 2. Now,

$$L(2.7) = L\left(\frac{27}{10}\right) = 3L(3) - L(2) - L(5) = .99324,$$

so that $e > 2.7$; and $L(2.8) = L\left(\dfrac{14}{5}\right) = L(2) + L(7) - L(5) = 1.02962$, so that $e < 2.8$. Thus,

$$2.7 < e < 2.8.$$

Also, e is nearer 2.7 than 2.8. To compute L(2.71), note that $2.71 = \dfrac{271}{270} \cdot \dfrac{27}{10}$, so that $L(2.71) = L\left(\dfrac{271}{270}\right) + L(2.7) = .99694$, so that $e > 2.71$; and $L(2.72) = L\left(\dfrac{272}{271}\right) + L\left(\dfrac{271}{270}\right) + L(2.7) = 1.00062$, so that

$$2.71 < e < 2.72.$$

It may be shown that e = 2.71828, to five decimal places.

SLOPE OF A SIMPLE GRAPH

The statement that the point P is *between* the simple graph f and the simple graph g means that, if P = (x,y), then the ordinate y of P is between $f(x)$ and $g(x)$.

The statement that the simple graph f *has slope at the point* P means that P is a point of f such that each two vertical lines with P between them have between them a point of f distinct from P, and that there exists a number m such that, if A is a straight line of slope greater than m containing P, and if B is a straight line of slope less than m containing P, then there exist vertical lines $h\,|$ and $k\,|$ with P between them such that every point of f distinct from P between $h\,|$ and $k\,|$ is between A and B.

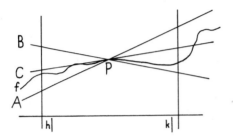

If the simple graph f has slope at the point P, then there is only one number m having the property described in the definition. This number m is called the *slope* of f at P; and the straight line of slope m containing P is called the *tangent line* to f at P.

Theorem. If the simple graph f has slope at the point P, if each two vertical lines with P between them have between them a point of f to the left of P and a point of f to the right of P, and if g is a straight line containing P such that no point of f is above g, then g is the tangent line to f at P.

Theorem. Suppose that f is a simple graph, that P is the point $(x, f(x))$ of f such that each two vertical lines with P between them have between them a point of f distinct from P, and that m is a number. The following two statements are equivalent:

   (i) f has slope m at P,

and

   (ii) if c is a positive number, there exists a positive number d such that, if y is the abscissa of a point of f whose distance from x is less than d, then

$$f(y) - f(x) = (y - x) \cdot {}'m + (y - x) \cdot \begin{bmatrix} \text{a number between} \\ -c \text{ and } c \end{bmatrix}.$$

Suggestion. Recall that, if u and v are numbers, then the number x is *between* u and v only in case there is a number t between 0 and 1 such that $x = (1 - t) \cdot u + t \cdot v$.

Examples.

(i) If x is a number and y a number,

$$y^2 - x^2 = (y - x) \cdot 2x + (y - x) \cdot [y - x].$$

Hence, if c is a positive number and y differs from x by less than c,

$$y^2 - x^2 = (y - x) \cdot 2x + (y - x) \cdot \begin{bmatrix} \text{a number between} \\ -c \text{ and } c \end{bmatrix}$$

Thus, the simple graph W defined, for each number x, by $W(x) = x^2$ has slope $2x$ at the point (x, x^2).

(ii) If x and y are positive numbers,

$$H(y) - H(x) = (y - x) \cdot \left[-\left(\frac{1}{x}\right)^2 \right] + (y - x) \cdot \left[\frac{x - y}{x^2 y} \right].$$

If c is a positive number and d a positive number less than both $\frac{x}{2}$ and $\frac{cx^3}{2}$, then, if y differs from x by less than d,

$$H(y) - H(x) = (y - x) \cdot \left[-\left(\frac{1}{x}\right)^2 \right] + (y - x) \cdot \begin{bmatrix} \text{a number between} \\ -c \text{ and } c \end{bmatrix}.$$

Thus, H has slope $-(1/x)^2$ at the point $(x, H(x))$.

In these examples, we had reason to believe that, if the graphs had slopes, then $2x$ was the slope of the first and $-(1/x)^2$ that of the second. We have verified that the graphs have these slopes. How should we proceed in case we have no previous knowledge as to what the slope should be?

(iii) Consider the simple graph Q. If x and y are positive numbers,

$$Q(y) - Q(x) = \frac{[Q(y) - Q(x)][Q(y) + Q(x)]}{Q(y) + Q(x)} = \frac{y - x}{Q(y) + Q(x)}.$$

Thus, if $U = (x, Q(x))$ and $V = (y, Q(y))$, the slope of the straight line containing U and V is

$$\frac{Q(y) - Q(x)}{y - x} = \frac{1}{Q(y) + Q(x)}$$

(See figure). The nearer y is to x, the nearer this slope is to $\frac{1}{2Q(x)}$, so that we conjecture that the slope of Q at the point U is $\frac{1}{2Q(x)}$. We then write,

$$Q(y) - Q(x) = (y - x) \cdot \frac{1}{Q(y) + Q(x)}$$

$$= (y - x) \cdot \frac{1}{2Q(x)} + (y - x) \cdot \left[\frac{1}{Q(y) + Q(x)} - \frac{1}{2Q(x)} \right]$$

$$= (y - x) \cdot \frac{1}{2Q(x)} + (y - x) \cdot \frac{Q(x) - Q(y)}{[Q(y) + Q(x)] 2Q(x)}$$

$$= (y - x) \cdot \frac{1}{2Q(x)} + (y - x) \cdot \frac{x - y}{[Q(y) + Q(x)][Q(y) + Q(x)] 2Q(x)},$$

from which it is easy to prove that our conjecture is correct. In fact, if c is a positive number and $d = c \cdot 2[Q(x)]^3$, then, if y is a positive number which differs from x by less than d,

$$Q(y) - Q(x) = (y - x) \cdot \frac{1}{2Q(x)} + (y - x) \cdot \left[\begin{array}{c} \text{a number between} \\ -c \text{ and } c \end{array} \right] .$$

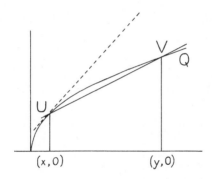

Definition.   If f is a simple graph, $D_x f$ denotes the slope of f at the point of f whose abscissa is x.

Examples.

$$D_x W = 2x,$$

$$D_x H = -\left(\frac{1}{x} \right)^2,$$

$$D_x Q = \frac{1}{2Q(x)} .$$

Exercise.   Show that $D_x L = \frac{1}{x}$ and $D_x E = E(x)$.

THE SIMPLE GRAPH I

The simple graph I is the simple graph to which the point P belongs only if the ordinate of P is the abscissa of P:

$$I(x) = x, \text{ for every number } x.$$

This is the straight line of slope 1 containing the point (0,0):

$$D_x I = 1, \text{ for every number } x.$$

Combinations of Simple Graphs

ADDITION

The statement that $f + g$ is the *sum* of the simple graph f and the simple graph g means that there is a number common to the X-projection of f and the X-projection of g and $f + g$ is the simple graph whose X-projection is the common part of the X-projection of f and the X-projection of g such that, if x is in this common part, the ordinate of that point of $f + g$ whose abscissa is x is $f(x) + g(x)$; *i.e.*,

$$(f + g)(x) = f(x) + g(x).$$

Example.   If f is the subset of the horizontal line $\underline{1}$ whose X-projection is the set of all nonpositive numbers and g the subset of the horizontal line $\underline{2}$ whose X-projection is the set of all nonnegative numbers, then $f + g$ is the simple graph containing only the point $(0,3)$. In this case, f has slope 0 at $(0,1)$, g has slope 0 at $(0,2)$ but $f + g$ does not have slope at $(0,3)$.

Problem.   Suppose the simple graph f has slope m_1 at $(x, f(x))$, the simple graph g has slope m_2 at $(x, g(x))$ and each two vertical lines with $(x, f(x) + g(x))$ between them have between them a point of $f + g$ distinct from $(x, f(x) + g(x))$. Find the slope $D_x (f + g)$.

MULTIPLICATION

The statement that fg or $f \cdot g$ is the *product* of the simple graph f and the simple graph g means that there is a number common to the X-projection of f and the X-projection of g and that $f \cdot g$ is the simple graph defined for every number x common to the X-projection of f and

33

the X-projection of g by

$$(f \cdot g)(x) = f(x) \cdot g(x).$$

Problem. Suppose f and g as in the preceding problem. Find the slope $D_x(f \cdot g)$.

BRACKET MULTIPLICATION

The statement that $f[g]$ (read f *of* g) is the *bracket product f* of g means there is a number x such that $g(x)$ is the abscissa of a point of f and $f[g]$ is defined for all such x by

$$f[g](x) = f(g(x)).$$

That is, the ordinate of that point of $f[g]$ whose abscissa is x is the ordinate of that point of f whose abscissa is $g(x)$.

There is a simple construction by which points of $f[g]$ may be located, shown in the accompanying figure.

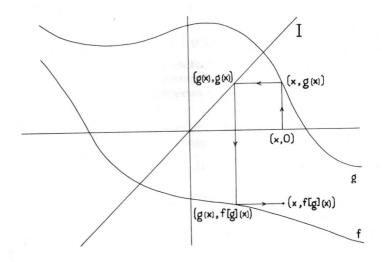

Starting with a point $(x,0)$, where x is the abscissa of a point of g, draw a vertical line interval to the point $(x,g(x))$ of g, then a horizontal line interval to the point $(g(x),g(x))$ of the simple graph I, then a vertical line interval to the point $(g(x),f[g](x))$ of f and, finally, draw a horizontal line interval to the point $(x,f[g](x))$ on the vertical line x l.

Problem. Suppose the simple graph g has slope m_2 at $(x, g(x))$ and the simple graph f has slope m at $(g(x), f[g](x))$. Suppose each two vertical lines with $(x, f[g](x))$ between them have between them a point of $f[g]$ distinct from $(x, f[g](x))$. Find the slope,

$$D_x f [g].$$

DIVISION

The reciprocal $1/g$ of the simple graph g is $F[g]$, where F is the simple graph defined, for every number x distinct from 0, by

$$F(x) = \frac{1}{x}.$$

Then, the quotient f/g of the simple graph f by the simple graph g is $f \cdot (1/g)$. A number x is not in the X-projection of $1/g$ in case $g(x) = 0$.

Problem. Suppose the simple graph g has slope m at $(x, g(x))$ and $g(x) \neq 0$. Find the slope

$$D_x \frac{1}{g}.$$

Then, under suitable conditions on the simple graph f, find

$$D_x \frac{f}{g}.$$

Statements analogous to some of the axioms of the number system are true for the system of simple graphs, complicated somewhat by the fact that two simple graphs may not have the same X-projection. If X_f denotes the X-projection of the simple graph f, some of these statements are as follows:

(i) If each of f, g, and h is a simple graph and X_f, X_g, and X_h have a common part, then $(f + g) + h = f + (g + h)$.

(ii) $\underline{0}$ is a simple graph such that, if f is a simple graph, $\underline{0} + f = f$.

(iii) If f is a simple graph, the simple graph $-f$ defined for every x in X_f by $(-f)(x) = -f(x)$, has the property that $f + (-f)$, denoted by $f - f$, is $\underline{0}f$.

(iv) If each of f and g is a simple graph and X_f and X_g have a common part, then $f + g = g + f$.

If k is a number, we ordinarily write kf for $\underline{k}f$ and $k + f$ for $\underline{k} + f$, for any simple graph f. If each of f and g is a simple graph and X_f and X_g have a common part, then $f + (-g)$ is written $f - g$ and called the *difference f minus g*.

The bracket product has interesting properties of which we mention a few. Suppose f is a simple graph. Then,

   (i) $f[I] = I[f] = f$,

   (ii) $f[\underline{1}] = f(1)$, if 1 is in X_f,

   (iii) $\underline{1}[f]$ is the subset of $\underline{1}$ whose X-projection is X_f,

   (iv) $\overline{L}[\underline{1}]$ is $\underline{0}$, and

   (v) $\underline{1}[\overline{L}]$ is the subset of $\underline{1}$ whose X-projection is the set of positive numbers.

If f is a simple graph, f^0 denotes $\underline{1}$ and, if n is a positive integer, $f^n = f \cdot f^{n-1}$.

THE DERIVATIVE

The statement that f' is the *derivative* of the simple graph f means that f has slope at one of its points and that f' is the simple graph to which the point (x,y) belongs only if f has slope at $(x, f(x))$ and y is the slope of f at $(x, f(x))$.

Examples.

$$H' = -H^2,$$

$$(I^2)' = 2I,$$

$$L' = H,$$

$$E' = E,$$

$$Q' = \frac{1}{2Q}.$$

If k is a number, $k' = 0$.

Under suitable conditions, *e.g.*, if f, g, f' and g' have X-projection an interval $[a,b]$, we have the following formulas:

   (i) $(f + g)' = f' + g'$,

   (ii) $(fg)' = fg' + f'g$,

   (iii) $(kf)' = kf'$, if k is a number.

Also, under suitable conditions:

   (iv) $(f[g])' = f'[g] \cdot g'$,

   (v) $\left(\dfrac{1}{g}\right)' = \dfrac{-g'}{(g^2)}$

and

   (vi) $\left(\dfrac{f}{g}\right)' = \dfrac{gf' - fg'}{g^2}$.

Exercise. Show that, if the simple graph f has slope at one of its points and n is a positive integer,

$$(f^n)' = nf^{n-1} \cdot f'.$$

If f is a simple graph, the absolute value of f, denoted by $|f|$, is the simple graph $Q[f^2]$. There is the formula,

$$|f|' = \frac{ff'}{|f|} \ .$$

Problem.   Each of the following sketches represents a simple graph f with X-projection the interval $[a,b]$, with $f(a)$ and $f(b)$ the number 0. Study these figures and then try to complete the statement below.

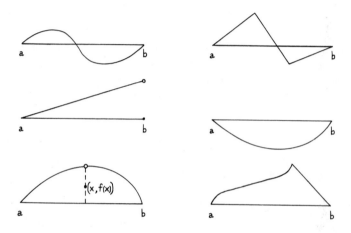

Statement.   If the simple graph f has X-projection the interval $[a,b]$, $f(a) = 0$, $f(b) = 0$, and f has slope at each of its points, then . . ..

Theorems about Simple Graphs

We now state a theorem about simple graphs followed by a number of other theorems which, since they may be proved on the basis of the main theorem, are labeled *corollaries*. We suggest that the reader take the main theorem for granted temporarily and use it as an axiom to prove the corollaries. He may then return to the main theorem from time to time until he succeeds in proving it.

Theorem. If the simple graph f has X-projection the interval $[a,b]$ and has slope at each of its points, then there is a point P of f such that no point of f is higher than P and a point Q of f such that no point of f is lower than Q.

Corollary 1. If the simple graph f has X-projection the interval $[a,b]$, $f(a) = 0$ and $f(b) = 0$, and f has slope at each of its points, then there exists a number c *between* a and b such that f has slope 0 at $(c,f(c))$:

$$D_c f = 0.$$

Corollary 2. Suppose each of f and g is a simple graph with X-projection the interval $[a,b]$ each having slope at each of its points, $f(a) = g(a)$ and $f(b) = g(b)$. Then there exists a number c between a and b such that

$$D_c f = D_c g.$$

Note. If, in particular, g is a straight line, the last equation may be written,

$$\frac{f(b) - f(a)}{b - a} = f'(c)$$

or

$$f(b) - f(a) = (b - a) \cdot f'(c).$$

Corollary 3. If the simple graph f has X-projection the interval $[a,b]$ and the slope of f is 0 at each of its points, then $f(x) = f(a)$ for every number x in $[a,b]$.

Corollary 4. Suppose f is a simple graph whose X-projection is the interval $[a,b]$ having slope at each of its points and there is a number c between a and b such that

$$f'(x) \begin{cases} < 0, & \text{if } a \leq x < c, \\ = 0, & \text{if } x = c, \\ > 0, & \text{if } c < x \leq b. \end{cases}$$

Then, the point $(c, f(c))$ is lower than any other point of f.

Note. There is, of course, an analogous condition for a point to be the highest point of f.

Corollary 5. Suppose each of f and g is a simple graph with X-projection the interval $[a,b]$ having slope at each of its points, $f(a) = g(a)$, $f(b) > g(b)$, and $D_b f < D_b g$. Then, there exists a number c between a and b such that $D_c f = D_c g$.

Corollary 6. Suppose each of f and g is a simple graph with X-projection $[a,b]$ having slope at each of its points, $f(a) = g(a)$ and, if x is a number between a and b, $D_x f > D_x g$. Then, $f(b) > g(b)$.

Corollary 7. Suppose the simple graph f has X-projection the interval $[a,b]$ and has slope at each of its points. If m is a number between $D_a f$ and $D_b f$, then there exists a number c between a and b such that $D_c f = m$.

THE CONJECTURED COMPUTATION FORMULA

In an earlier chapter, we conjectured that, if c is a number greater than 1 and n a positive integer,

$$L(c) = \frac{c-1}{c} + \frac{1}{2}\left(\frac{c-1}{c}\right)^2 + \ldots + \frac{1}{n}\left(\frac{c-1}{c}\right)^n + k_n,$$

$$0 < k_n < \frac{1}{n+1}\left(\frac{c-1}{c}\right)^{n+1} \cdot c.$$

To establish this, we suggest that the reader adopt a more general point of view and consider the simple graph K_n defined by

39

$$K_n = L - (1 - H) - \frac{1}{2}(1 - H)^2 - \ldots - \frac{1}{n}(1 - H)^n,$$

so that the number k_n is $K_n(c)$. Two applications of Corollary 6 with suitable choices of f and g in each case will now establish the conjecture to be true.

THE ADDITION FORMULAS FOR L AND E

We had the formulas

$$L(cx) = L(c) + L(x)$$

and

$$E(c + x) = E(c)E(x),$$

the first being true for $c > 0$ and $x > 0$ and the second for any number c and any number x. These formulas may be called *addition formulas*. These formulas may be proved by adopting a "more general point of view" and using Corollary 3. Note that the first formula may be stated as follows: the simple graph f defined by

$$f = L[cI] - L - L(c)$$

is a subset of $\underline{0}$; and the second may be stated: the simple graph f defined by

$$f = \frac{E[c + I]}{E(c) \cdot E}$$

is the horizontal line $\underline{1}$.

THE SIMPLE GRAPHS S AND $\mathscr{C}$

These are defined as follows:

$$S = \frac{1}{2}\left\{E - \frac{1}{E}\right\} \text{ and } \mathscr{C} = \frac{1}{2}\left\{E + \frac{1}{E}\right\}.$$

Since $\frac{1}{E(x)} = E(-x)$, for every number x, we see that the point (x,y) belongs to the simple graph $1/E$ only if the point $(-x,y)$ belongs to E. To sketch S and $\mathscr{C}$, simply sketch E and $1/E$ and then take half their difference and then half their sum.

Exercise
(i) Show that $S' = \mathscr{C}$ and $\mathscr{C}' = S$.
(ii) Show that $\mathscr{C}^2 - S^2 = \underline{1}$.

(iii) Show that if x is a number and c a number:

$$S(x + c) = S(x)\,\mathcal{C}(c) + \mathcal{C}(x)\,S(c)$$

and

$$\mathcal{C}(x + c) = \mathcal{C}(x)\,\mathcal{C}(c) + S(x)\,S(c).$$

The derivative of f', $(f')'$, is denoted by f'' and called the *second derivative* of f.

(iv) Show that $S'' = S$ and $\mathcal{C}'' = \mathcal{C}$.

(v) Sketch the simple graphs $\mathcal{K}$ and $\mathcal{T}$ defined by

$$\mathcal{K} = \frac{1}{\mathcal{C}} \quad \text{and} \quad \mathcal{T} = \frac{S}{\mathcal{C}}.$$

(vi) Show that $\mathcal{T}' = \mathcal{K}^2$ and $\mathcal{K}' = -\mathcal{K}\mathcal{T}$. Also, $\mathcal{T}' = 1 - \mathcal{T}^2$.

(vii) Show that, if x is a number and y a number,

$$\mathcal{T}(x + y) = \frac{\mathcal{T}(x) + \mathcal{T}(y)}{1 + \mathcal{T}(x)\,\mathcal{T}(y)}.$$

(viii) Show that if x and y are numbers and $x < y$, then $\mathcal{T}(x) < \mathcal{T}(y)$.

(ix) Show that every point of the simple graph $\mathcal{T}$ is between the horizontal lines -1 and 1. Moreover, show that 1 is the least positive number k such that each point of $\mathcal{T}$ is between $-k$ and k.

$\mathcal{A}$ denotes the simple graph to which the point (x,y) belongs only if the point (y,x) belongs to $\mathcal{T}$. The X-projection of $\mathcal{A}$ is the set of all numbers between -1 and 1.

Exercise

(i) Show that $D_x\,\mathcal{A} = \dfrac{1}{1 - x^2}$, $-1 < x < 1$.

(ii) Show that if c is a number between -1 and 1, the simple graph $\mathcal{A} + \mathcal{A}(c) - \mathcal{A}\left[\dfrac{I + c}{1 + Ic}\right]$ is a subset of $\underline{0}$, so that, if x is a number between -1 and 1,

$$\mathcal{A}(x) + \mathcal{A}(c) = \mathcal{A}\left(\frac{x + c}{1 + xc}\right).$$

(iii) Show that

$$\mathcal{A} = \frac{1}{2}L\left[\frac{1 + I}{1 - I}\right].$$

A POINT SET WHICH IS NOT A SIMPLE GRAPH

Suppose G denotes the point set to which (x,y) belongs only if $y^2 = x^2(1 - x^2)$. There are two points of G having the same abscissa, so that G is not a simple graph. The points of G constitute two simple graphs:

$$\text{IQ}[1 - \text{I}^2] \text{ and } -\text{IQ}[1 - \text{I}^2].$$

Denote the first of these by f.
The X-projection of f is $[-1,1]$.

Exercise. Calculate f', find the highest point of f, the lowest point of f and sketch f and then G. Show that

$$f'' = \frac{\text{I}(2\text{I}^2 - 3)}{(1 - \text{I}^2)\text{Q}[1 - \text{I}^2]} .$$

Note that $f''(x)$ is positive, 0, or negative according as $-1 < x < 0$, $x = 0$, or $0 < x < 1$, respectively. Does this signify anything concerning the shape of f? Does f have slope 1.001 at any of its points?

INEQUALITIES

Theorem. If the simple graph f has X-projection the interval $[a,b]$, if f'', the second derivative of f, has X-projection $[a,b]$, and if $f''(x) > 0$ for every number x between a and b, then every point of f with abscissa between a and b is below the line containing the points $(a,f(a))$ and $(b,f(b))$. That is,

$$f(x) < \frac{f(b) - f(a)}{b - a} (x - a) + f(a), \qquad \text{if } a < x < b$$

Suppose k is a positive number distinct from 1, and f is the simple graph defined, for every number x, by

$$f(x) = k^x.$$

Thus, $f = \text{E}[\text{IL}(k)]$. Then, $f' = \text{E}'[\text{IL}(k)] \cdot \{\text{IL}(k)\}' = f \cdot \text{L}(k)$, and $f'' = f \cdot \text{L}^2(k)$, so that $f''(x) > 0$ for every number x. Thus, if we take $[a,b]$ to be $[0,1]$ we have, by the Theorem,

$$k^x < (k - 1) \cdot x + 1, \qquad \text{if } 0 < x < 1,$$

or

$$k^x < k \cdot x + (1 - x), \qquad \text{if } 0 < x < 1.$$

If a and b are positive numbers and $k = a/b$, the inequality may be written,

42

$$a^x \cdot b^{1-x} < a \cdot x + b \cdot (1 - x), \qquad \text{if } 0 < x < 1.$$

If, in particular, $x = (1/2)$, this becomes,

$$\sqrt{a \cdot b} < \frac{a + b}{2}.$$

That is, the "geometric mean" of two positive numbers is less than their "arithmetic mean."

Suppose, next, that each of a, b, and c is a positive number and $b \neq c$ and each of x, y, and z is a positive number and $x + y + z = 1$. Then,

$$a^x \cdot b^y \cdot c^z = a^x \cdot \left\{ b^{\frac{y}{y+z}} \cdot c^{\frac{z}{y+z}} \right\}^{y+z} \leq a \cdot x + \left\{ b^{\frac{y}{y+z}} \cdot c^{\frac{z}{y+z}} \right\} \cdot (y + z)$$

and, therefore,

$$a^x \cdot b^y \cdot c^z < x \cdot a + y \cdot b + z \cdot c.$$

If $x = y = z = \frac{1}{3}$, this gives

$$\sqrt[3]{abc} < \frac{a + b + c}{3}.$$

The reader may follow this up and find many other inequalities.

The Simple Graphs of Trigonometry

Following a pattern analogous to that by which the simple graphs L and E were developed from H, simple graphs A and T may be developed from Ω, where (See figure)

$$\Omega = \frac{1}{1 + I^2} \cdot$$

There are enough differences and similarities between the two developments to make the work interesting. We shall give a broad outline, leaving the details to be carried through by the reader.

If $[a,b]$ is an interval, we denote by $[\Omega;a,b]$ the point set to which (x,y) belongs only if x belongs to $[a,b]$ and y is 0, y is $\frac{1}{1 + x^2}$, or y is a number between 0 and $\frac{1}{1 + x^2}$. An inner sum for $[\Omega;a,b]$ is the sum of the areas of finitely many nonoverlapping rectangular intervals included in $[\Omega;a,b]$, their bases filling up $[a,b]$ and each one as high as possible. The accompanying figure shows three such rectangular intervals.

The area of $[\Omega;a,b]$, denoted by $\int_a^b \Omega$, is the least number which no inner sum for $[\Omega;a,b]$ exceeds.

A denotes the simple graph whose X-projection is the set of all numbers defined by

$$A(x) = \begin{cases} -\int_x^0 \Omega, & \text{if } x < 0, \\ 0, & \text{if } x = 0, \\ \int_0^x \Omega, & \text{if } x > 0. \end{cases}$$

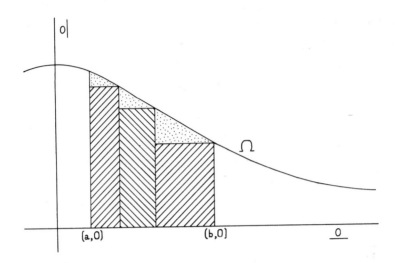

If (x,y) is a point of A, then $(-x,-y)$ is a point of A.

If $[p,q]$ is an interval of nonnegative numbers, we have the approximation,

$$\int_p^q \Omega = \frac{q - p}{2} \cdot \frac{p^2 + q^2 + 2}{(1 + p^2)(1 + q^2)} ,$$

with error less than

$$\frac{(q - p)^2}{2} \cdot \frac{q + p}{(1 + p^2)(1 + q^2)} .$$

As in the case of L, this formula may be used to compute a table of values,

x	$A(x)$
0	0
.1	.0995
.2	.1971
.3	.2911
.4	
.5	
.6	
.7	
.8	
.9	
1.0	

by means of the following theorem.

Theorem. If $[a,b]$ is an interval and c a number between a and b, then

$$\int_a^b \Omega = \int_a^c \Omega + \int_c^b \Omega ;$$

and

$$A(b) - A(a) = \int_a^b \Omega .$$

It follows that, if x and y are nonnegative numbers or if x and y are nonpositive numbers, then $A(y) - A(x)$ is between $(y - x)\, \Omega\, (x)$ and $(y - x)\Omega(y)$. That is, there exists a number t between 0 and 1 such that

$$A(y) - A(x) = (y - x)\{(1 - t) \cdot \Omega(x) + t \cdot \Omega(y)\}$$

or

$$A(y) - A(x) = (y - x) \cdot \Omega(x) + (y - x) \cdot t \cdot \{\Omega(y) - \Omega(x)\}.$$

Consequently, $D_x A = \Omega(x)$ or $A' = \Omega$.

Problem. Show that, if x is a number, $-3 < A(x) < 3$.

We denote by $\pi/2$ the least positive number k such that the simple graph A is between the horizontal lines $-k$ and k.

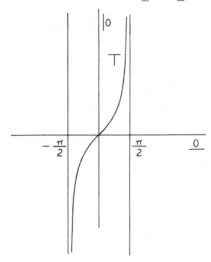

If x and y are numbers and $x < y$, then $A(x) < A(y)$; and the Y-projection of A is the set of all numbers between $-\pi/2$ and $\pi/2$.

The point set to which (x,y) belongs only if (y,x) belongs to A is a simple graph which we denote by T. The X-projection of T is the set of all numbers between $-\pi/2$ and $\pi/2$. The derivative of T is $1 + T^2$:

$$T' = 1 + T^2 .$$

ADDITION FORMULAS FOR A

There are some analogies between the graphs $\mathcal{A}$ and A. For instance, we have:

$$D_x \mathcal{A} = \frac{1}{1 - x^2} \text{ and } D_x A = \frac{1}{1 + x^2} ,$$

and

$$\mathcal{T}' = 1 - \mathcal{T}^2 \text{ and } T' = 1 + T^2 .$$

If each of x and c is a number between -1 and 1,

$$\mathcal{A}(x) + \mathcal{A}(c) = \mathcal{A}\left(\frac{x + c}{1 + xc}\right).$$

This is analogous to the formula

$$L(x) + L(c) = L(xc), \quad (x > 0, c > 0).$$

A study of the simple graph A shows that there are numbers x and c such that $A(x) + A(c)$ is not the ordinate of any point of A. For instance, this appears to be the situation if $x > 1$ and $c > 1$. On the other hand, if $xc < 1$, it would seem that $A(x) + A(c)$ is the ordinate of some point of A. We conjecture, by analogy with the addition formula for $\mathcal{A}$, that, if each of x and c is a number and $xc < 1$, then

$$A(x) + A(c) = A\left(\frac{x + c}{1 - xc}\right).$$

To adopt a more general point of view, the question to be decided is as follows. If c is a number, the simple graph f defined by

$$f = A + \underline{A(c)} - A\left[\frac{I + c}{1 - Ic}\right],$$

whose X-projection is the set of all numbers x for which $cx \neq 1$, *has slope 0 at each of its points*. Since $f(0) = 0$, it follows that $f(x) = 0$ if

$cx < 1$, *which is our conjecture*; and there exists a number k such that $f(x) = k$ if $cx > 1$.

Exercise. Show that, if x is a number, then

(i) $A(x) + A\left(\dfrac{1}{x}\right) = \begin{cases} \dfrac{\pi}{2}, & \text{if } x > 0, \\[2mm] -\dfrac{\pi}{2}, & \text{if } x < 0. \end{cases}$

(ii) $A(x) + A(1) = A\left(\dfrac{1 + x}{1 - x}\right),$ if $x < 1,$

(iii) $A(x) - A(1) = A\left(\dfrac{x - 1}{x + 1}\right),$ if $x > -1,$

(iv) $A(x) + A(c) - A\left(\dfrac{x + c}{1 - xc}\right) = \begin{cases} \pi, & \text{if } xc > 1 \text{ and } x > 0, \\ -\pi, & \text{if } xc > 1 \text{ and } x < 0. \end{cases}$

We include the formula previously stated:

(v) $A(x) + A(c) = A\left(\dfrac{x + c}{1 - xc}\right),$ if $xc < 1.$

Show that, if each of x and y is a number between $-\pi/2$ and $\pi/2$ such that $x + y$ is between $-\pi/2$ and $\pi/2$, then
$$T(x + y) = \frac{T(x) + T(y)}{1 - T(x)T(y)}.$$

Problem. Show that $T(\pi/4) = 1$.

COMPUTATION PROBLEM FOR A

If x is a number, $A(-x) = -A(x)$ and $A(0) = 0$, so that it suffices to consider the computation problem for $A(x)$ only in case $x > 0$.

If c is a positive number, $A(c) = \int_0^c \Omega > c \cdot \dfrac{1}{1 + c^2}$, so that $A(c)$

$= \dfrac{c}{1 + c^2} + (\text{a positive number})$. Let A_1 denote the simple graph defined by
$$A_1 = A - \frac{I}{1 + I^2}.$$

Then, this positive number is $A_1(c)$. We find that
$$A_1' = \frac{2I^2}{(1 + I^2)^2},$$

so that, if $0 < x < c$, $D_x A_1 > D_x 0$. Inasmuch as $A_1(0) = 0(0)$, it follows from an earlier theorem that $A_1(c) > 0$. We next seek a simple graph g such that $A_1(0) = g(0)$ and, if $0 < x < c$, $D_x A_1 < D_x g$. After some experimentation, we find that such a simple graph g is

$$c \cdot \frac{I^2}{1 + I^2} ,$$

and, consequently,

$$0 < A_1(c) < \frac{c}{1 + c^2} \cdot c^2 ,$$

$$A(c) = \frac{c}{1 + c^2} + A_1(c) .$$

The fact that $A(x) = -A(-x)$ for every number x, so that $A_1(x) = -A_1(-x)$ for every number x, might lead us to try next something such as,

$$A(c) = \frac{c}{1 + c^2} + \frac{ac^3}{(1 + c^2)^2} + A_2(c) ,$$

where a is a positive number. (If $a < 0$, the new formula wouldn't be as good as the one already found.) If

$$A_2 = A - \frac{I}{1 + I^2} - \frac{aI^3}{(1 + I^2)^2} = A_1 - \frac{aI^3}{(1 + I^2)^2} ,$$

then

$$A_2' = A_1' - \frac{(1 + I^2)^2 \cdot 3aI^2 - aI^3 \cdot 2(1 + I^2) \cdot 2I}{(1 + I^2)^4} = \frac{(2 - 3a)I^2 + (2 + a)I^4}{(1 + I^2)^3} .$$

This suggests that we choose a to be $2/3$, so that

$$A_2' = \frac{8}{3} \cdot \frac{I^4}{(1 + I^2)^3} .$$

Then, $A_2(c) > 0$ and, we find after some experimentation, that a simple graph g for which $g(0) = A_2(0)$ and $D_x A_2 < D_x g$ for $0 < x < c$ is

$$\frac{2}{3} c \cdot \left(\frac{I^2}{1 + I^2} \right)^2 .$$

Consequently,

$$0 < A_2(c) < \frac{2}{3} \cdot \frac{c^3}{(1 + c^2)^2} \cdot c^2 ,$$

$$A(c) = \frac{c}{1 + c^2} + \frac{2}{3} \cdot \frac{c^3}{(1 + c^2)^2} + A_2(c) .$$

We have now found

$$A_1 = A - \frac{I}{1 + I^2} \text{ and } A_1' = \frac{2}{1} \cdot \frac{I^2}{(1 + I^2)^2};$$

$$A_2 = A_1 - \frac{2}{3} \cdot \frac{I^3}{(1 + I^2)^2} \text{ and } A_2' = \frac{2}{1} \cdot \frac{4}{3} \cdot \frac{I^4}{(1 + I^2)^3};$$

and we conjecture

$$A_3 = A_2 - \frac{2}{3} \cdot \frac{4}{5} \cdot \frac{I^5}{(1 + I^2)^3} \text{ and } A_3' = \frac{2}{1} \cdot \frac{4}{3} \cdot \frac{6}{5} \cdot \frac{I^6}{(1 + I^2)^4},$$

and so on; and, if n is a positive integer,

$$A(c) = \frac{c}{1 + c^2} + \frac{2}{3} \cdot \frac{c^3}{(1 + c^2)^2} + \cdots + \frac{2}{3} \cdot \frac{4}{5} \cdot \cdots \cdot \frac{2n}{2n+1} \cdot \frac{c^{2n+1}}{(1 + c^2)^{n+1}}$$

$$+ A_n(c), \text{ where } 0 < A_n(c) < \frac{2}{3} \cdot \frac{4}{5} \cdot \cdots \cdot \frac{2n}{2n+1} \cdot \frac{c^{2n+1}}{(1 + c^2)^{n+1}} \cdot c^2.$$

This is a true statement.

Taking c to be 1, we find that A(1) = .7854, to four decimal places, and consequently π, or 4A(1), is 3.1416, to four decimal places.

THE SIMPLE GRAPHS K, C, S, AND B

The simple graph K whose X-projection is the set of all numbers between $-\pi/2$ and $\pi/2$ is defined by

$$K = Q[1 + T^2].$$

The simple graph C whose X-projection is the interval $[-\pi/2, \pi/2]$ is defined by

$$C(x) = \begin{cases} 0, & \text{if } x = -\frac{\pi}{2}, \\ \dfrac{1}{K(x)}, & \text{if } -\frac{\pi}{2} < x < \frac{\pi}{2}, \\ 0, & \text{if } x = \frac{\pi}{2}. \end{cases}$$

The simple graph S whose X-projection is the interval $[-\pi/2, \pi/2]$ is defined by

$$S(x) = \begin{cases} -1, & \text{if } x = -\frac{\pi}{2}, \\ C(x)T(x), & \text{if } -\frac{\pi}{2} < x < \frac{\pi}{2}, \\ 1, & \text{if } x = \frac{\pi}{2}. \end{cases}$$

Exercise.   Show that the following statements are true:
  (i) $T' = K^2$,
 (ii) $K' = KT$,
(iii) $S' = C$ and $C' = -S$,
 (iv) $C^2 + S^2$ is a subset of $\underline{1}$,
  (v) $T = \dfrac{S}{C}$,
and
  (vi) if each of u and v is a number in the interval $[-\pi/2, \pi/2]$ such that $u + v$ is in this interval, then $S(u + v) = S(u)C(v) + C(u)S(v)$ and $C(u + v) = C(u)C(v)-S(u)S(v)$.

The Y-projection of S is the interval $[-1, 1]$ and, if x and y are numbers in this interval such that $x < y$, then $S(x) < S(y)$. It follows that the point set B to which (x,y) belongs only if (y,x) belongs to S is a simple graph whose X-projection is $[-1, 1]$. The Y-projection of B is, of course, $[-\pi/2, \pi/2]$.

If x is a number between -1 and 1,

$$D_x\, B = \frac{1}{Q[1 - x^2]} \; ;$$

i.e.,

$$B' = \frac{1}{Q[1 - I^2]} \; .$$

EXTENSION OF S AND C TO THE SET OF ALL NUMBERS

We now extend the simple graphs S and C so that their X-projections shall be the set of all numbers by simply requiring that the formulas

$$S(u + v) = S(u)C(v) + C(u)S(v),$$

$$C(u + v) = C(u)C(v) - S(u)S(v),$$

shall be true for all numbers. For this purpose, it is sufficient to require that

$$S(u + 2\pi) = S(u),$$

$$C(u + 2\pi) = C(u),$$

for every number u. We then extend the definition of K by the formula

$$K = \frac{1}{C} \; ,$$

and the definition of T by

$$T = \frac{S}{C}.$$

The formulas

$$S' = C, \ C' = -S, \ T' = K^2, \text{ and } K' = KT$$

are true for the extended simple graphs. Also,

$$C^2 + S^2 = \underline{1} \text{ and } 1 + T^2 = K^2.$$

We leave to the reader the project of filling in detailed proofs of the statements made in the preceding outline. One of the main problems is to show that the formulas

$$D_x \, C = -S(x) \text{ and } D_x \, S = C(x)$$

are true if $x = -(\pi/2)$ and $x = (\pi/2)$.

Exercise
(i) Find the derivatives of $L[\,|K|\,]$ and $L[\,|K + T|\,]$.
(ii) Show that

$$S[A] = \frac{I}{Q[1 + I^2]} \text{ and } C[A] = \frac{1}{Q[1 + I^2]}.$$

(iii) Show that $C[3I] = 4C^3 - 3C$ and use this to find $S(x)$, $C(x)$, $T(x)$, and $K(x)$ if $x = (\pi/6)$ and $x = (\pi/3)$.
(iv) Find $S(x)$, $C(x)$ and $K(x)$ if $x = (\pi/4)$.

CONNECTION WITH TRIANGLES

Theorem. If r is a positive number and each of x and y a number such that $x^2 + y^2 = r^2$, then there exists only one number θ such that $0 \le \theta < 2\pi$ and

$$S(\theta) = (y/r) \text{ and } C(\theta) = (x/r).$$

Definition. The number θ of the preceding theorem is called *the argument* of the point (x,y). That is, if (x,y) is a point such that $x^2 + y^2$ is the positive number r^2, $(r > 0)$, then the number θ such that $0 \le \theta < 2\pi$, $S(\theta) = (y/r)$, and $C(\theta) = (x/r)$ is the argument of (x,y).

If (x,y) is a point distinct from $(0,0)$ and t is a positive number, then the argument of (x,y) is the argument of (tx,ty). Since $T(\theta) = S(\theta)/C(\theta)$, then $T(\theta) = y/x$, provided $x \ne 0$. Thus, $T(\theta)$ is the slope of

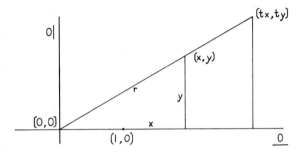

the straight line containing $(0,0)$ and (x,y). The number r is the *distance* from $(0,0)$ to (x,y). Thus, if $x > 0$ and $y > 0$, $S(\theta)$, $C(\theta)$, $T(\theta)$, and $K(\theta)$ are ratios of lengths of sides of a triangle:

$$S(\theta) = \frac{y}{r}, \quad C(\theta) = \frac{x}{r}, \quad T(\theta) = \frac{y}{x}, \quad K(\theta) = \frac{r}{x}.$$

There are two more ratios: $\dfrac{1}{S(\theta)}$ and $\dfrac{1}{T(\theta)}$.

PROPERTY (S)

Each of the following sketches shows a simple graph with one of its points designated with the letter P. Those simple graphs marked (Y) have property (S) at the point P and those marked (N) do not have property (S) at P. See if you can describe this property in terms of pairs of horizontal and vertical lines.

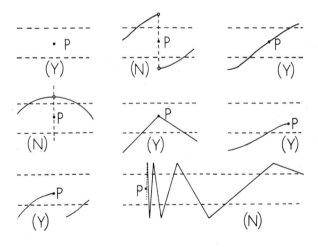

The Integral

The statement that the simple graph f *is bounded on the interval* $[a,b]$ means that the X-projection of f includes $[a,b]$ and that there exist horizontal lines α and β such that every point of f whose abscissa is in $[a,b]$ is between α and β.

Suppose the simple graph f is bounded on $[a,b]$. The statement that $_iS$ *is an inner sum for f on* $[a,b]$ means that there exists a finite collection D of nonoverlapping intervals filling up $[a,b]$ such that, if the length of each interval in D is multiplied by the largest number which exceeds the ordinate of no point of f whose abscissa is in that interval, then the sum of all the products so formed is $_iS$; the inner sum may be described as *based* on D and designated as $_iS_D$. The statement that $_oS$ *is an outer sum for f on* $[a,b]$ means that there exists a finite collection D of nonoverlapping intervals filling up $[a,b]$ such that, if the length of each interval in D is multiplied by the smallest number which the ordinate of no point of f with abscissa in that interval exceeds, then the sum of all the products so formed is $_oS$ or $_oS_D$ (See figure).

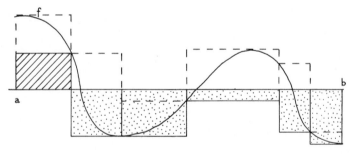

Since f is bounded on $[a,b]$, there is a number which no inner sum for f on $[a,b]$ exceeds. The *least* number which no inner sum for f on $[a,b]$ exceeds is denoted by

$$_i\!\int_a^b f$$

and called the *inner integral from a to b of f*. Similarly, there is a number which exceeds no outer sum for f on $[a,b]$. The *largest* number which exceeds no outer sum for f on $[a,b]$ is denoted by

$$_o\!\int_a^b f$$

and called the *outer integral from a to b of f*.

Theorem. Suppose the simple graph f is bounded on $[a,b]$ and each of α and β is a number such that, if x is a number in $[a,b]$, $\alpha \le f(x) \le \beta$. If $_iS$ is an inner sum for f on $[a,b]$ and $_oS$ an outer sum for f on $[a,b]$, then

$$(b - a) \cdot \alpha \le {}_iS \le {}_i\!\int_a^b f \le {}_o\!\int_a^b f \le {}_oS \le (b - a) \cdot \beta .$$

There exists a simple graph f which is bounded on the interval $[0,1]$ such that $_i\!\int_0^1 f = 0$ and $_o\!\int_0^1 f = 1$.

If $[a,b]$ is an interval of positive numbers, $_i\!\int_a^b H = {}_o\!\int_a^b H$; and, if $[a,b]$ is an interval, $_i\!\int_a^b \Omega = {}_o\!\int_a^b \Omega$.

Definition. The statement that the simple graph f is integrable on the interval $[a,b]$ means that f is bounded on $[a,b]$ and $_i\!\int_a^b f = {}_o\!\int_a^b f$. If the simple graph f is integrable on $[a,b]$, the number $_i\!\int_a^b f$, which is $_o\!\int_a^b f$, is denoted by $\int_a^b f$ and called *the integral from a to b of f*.

Theorem. Suppose the simple graph f is bounded on the interval $[a,b]$ and c is a number between a and b. Then,

$$_i\!\int_a^b f = {}_i\!\int_a^c f + {}_i\!\int_c^b f$$

and

$$_o\!\int_a^b f = {}_o\!\int_a^c f + {}_o\!\int_c^b f .$$

55

If

$$g(x) = \begin{cases} 0, & \text{if } x = a, \\ {}_i\!\int_a^x f, & \text{if } a < x \le b, \end{cases}$$

$$\text{and } h(x) = \begin{cases} 0, & \text{if } x = a, \\ {}_o\!\int_a^x f, & \text{if } a < x \le b, \end{cases}$$

then, if $[x,y]$ is a subinterval of $[a,b]$,

$$g(y) - g(x) = {}_i\!\int_x^y f \text{ and } h(y) - h(x) = {}_o\!\int_x^y f.$$

Question. Is it true that $g' = f$ and $h' = f$? (We had $L' = H$ and $A' = \Omega$.)

PROPERTY (S)

The statement that the simple graph f has property (S) at the point P means that P is a point of f and, if α and β are horizontal lines with P between them, there exist vertical lines $h|$ and $k|$ with P between them such that every point of f between $h|$ and $k|$ is between α and β.

Theorem. Suppose f, g, and h are as in the preceding theorem, and x is a number in $[a,b]$ such that f has property (S) at the point $(x, f(x))$. Then,

$$D_x g = f(x) \text{ and } D_x h = f(x).$$

If, in particular, f has X-projection $[a,b]$ and has property (S) at each of its points, then $g' = f$ and $h' = f$ and $g = h$, so that

$$_i\!\int_a^b f = {}_o\!\int_a^b f;$$

i.e., f is integrable on $[a,b]$.

If the simple graph f has slope at the point P, then f has property (S) at P; but there exists a simple graph f having property (S) at the point P which does not have slope at P.

If the reader has succeeded in proving the theorem on page 38, it may be that his proof can be modified to establish the following more general theorem. If not, we suggest that he work on the following theorem, which includes the theorem on page 38 as a corollary.

Theorem. If the simple graph f has X-projection the interval $[a,b]$ and has property (S) at each of its points, then there exists a point P of f such that no point of f is higher than P and a point Q of f such that no point of f is lower than Q.

Corollary 1. If the simple graph f has X-projection the interval $[a,b]$ and has property (S) at each of its points, then f is integrable on $[a,b]$.

Corollary 2. If the simple graph f has X-projection the interval $[a,b]$ and has property (S) at each of its points, then there exists a simple graph g with X-projection $[a,b]$ such that $g' = f$.

Corollary 3. Suppose f, P, and Q are as in the above theorem, and $\underline{h}$ is a horizontal line between P and Q. There exists a point of f belonging to $\underline{h}$.

The corollaries to the main theorem on page 38 may be somewhat improved. We state here an improved version of the first of those corollaries and suggest that the reader examine the others with a view toward improving them.

Theorem. If the simple graph f has X-projection the interval $[a,b]$ and has property (S) at each of its points, if $f(a) = 0$, and $f(b) = 0$, and if f has slope at each of its points with abscissa *between* a and b, then there exists a number c between a and b such that

$$D_c f = 0.$$

Problem. Under suitable hypotheses upon f and g, investigate the question of property (S) for $f + g$, $f \cdot g$, $f[g]$, and f/g.

PROPERTIES OF INTEGRALS

(i) If f is a simple graph such that f' is bounded on the interval $[a,b]$, then

$$_i\!\int_a^b f' \leq f(b) - f(a) \leq {_o}\!\int_a^b f',$$

so that, if f' is integrable on $[a,b]$,

$$\int_a^b f' = f(b) - f(a).$$

(ii) If each of f and g is a simple graph which is integrable on $[a,b]$ and if k is a number, then $f + g$ and kf are integrable on $[a,b]$ and

$$\int_a^b (f + g) = \int_a^b f + \int_a^b g \text{ and } \int_a^b kf = k \cdot \int_a^b f.$$

(iii) If each of f and g is integrable on $[a,b]$, then $f \cdot g$ is integrable on $[a,b]$.

(iv) If each of f, g, f', and g' is integrable on $[a,b]$, then

$$\int_a^b fg' = \int_a^b (fg)' - \int_a^b gf' = f(b)g(b) - f(a)g(a) - \int_a^b gf'.$$

(v) If f is integrable on $[a,b]$ and c is a number between a and b, then f is integrable on $[a,c]$ and on $[c,b]$ and

$$\int_a^b f = \int_a^c f + \int_c^b f.$$

EVALUATION OF INTEGRALS

In order to develop facility in evaluation of integrals, it is perhaps best to start out with the idea of using the preceding properties *to write an integral in different forms.* By (1) any integral which can be written as $\int_a^b f'$ can be evaluated as $f(b) - f(a)$.

Examples. $\int_a^b C = \int_a^b S' = S(b) - S(a); \int_a^b S = \int_a^b (-C)' = C(a) - C(b)$.

If f is a simple graph whose X-projection includes the interval $[a,b]$, $[f;a,b]$ denotes the point set to which (x,y) belongs only if x is in $[a,b]$ and $y = 0$, $y = f(x)$ or y is a number between 0 and $f(x)$. If $f(x) \geq 0$ for every number x in $[a,b]$, the area of $[f;a,b]$ is *defined* to be the integral $\int_a^b f$. For instance, the area of $[S;0,\pi/2]$ is $\int_0^{\pi/2} S = 2$.

Exercise 1. Evaluate each of the integrals:

(i) $\int_a^b \underline{k}$, *i.e.*, $\int_a^b (kI)'$,

(ii) $\int_a^b I$,

(iii) $\int_a^b I^2$,

(iv) $\int_a^b I^3$,

(v) $\int_a^b E$,

(vi) $\int_a^b S$,

(vii) $\int_a^b C$,

(viii) $\int_a^b K^2$,

(ix) $\int_a^b KT$,

(x) $\int_a^b \dfrac{1}{1 + I^2}$

and (xi) $\int_a^b \dfrac{1}{I}$.

The interval $[a,b]$ must be subject to a certain restriction in the case of (viii), (ix), and (xi).

The next examples illustrate the use of property (iv) to write integrals in different forms.

$$\int_a^b S^2 = \int_a^b SS = \int_a^b S \cdot (-C)' = \int_a^b (-SC)' - \int_a^b (-C)S'$$

$$= \int_a^b (-SC)' + \int_a^b C^2 = \int_a^b (-SC)' + \int_a^b (\underline{1} - S^2),$$

or

$$2\int_a^b S^2 = \int_a^b (-SC)' + \int_a^b I' = \int_a^b (I - SC)',$$

or

$$\int_a^b S^2 = \int_a^b \left\{ \frac{I - SC}{2} \right\}' .$$

For instance, the area of $[S^2; 0, \frac{\pi}{2}]$ is $\int_0^{\pi/2} S^2$ or $\frac{\pi}{4}$.

Next,

$$\int_a^b S^3 = \int_a^b S^2 S = \int_a^b S^2 \cdot (-C)' = \int_a^b (-CS^2)' - \int_a^b (-C)(S^2)'$$

$$= \int_a^b (-CS^2)' + \int_a^b C \cdot 2SS' = \int_a^b (-CS^2)' + 2\int_a^b C^2 S$$

$$= \int_a^b (-CS^2)' + 2\int_a^b (1 - S^2) \cdot S,$$

or

$$3\int_a^b S^3 = \int_a^b (-CS^2)' + 2\int_a^b (-C)' = \int_a^b \{ -CS^2 - 2C \}',$$

or

$$\int_a^b S^3 = \int_a^b \left\{ \frac{-CS^2 - 2C}{3} \right\}' .$$

Thus, $\int_0^{\pi/2} S^3 = \frac{2}{3}$.

Exercise 2. If n is a nonnegative integer, let k_n denote $\int_0^{\pi/2} S^n$. Then,

$$k_0 = \frac{\pi}{2}, \qquad\qquad k_2 = \frac{\pi}{2} \cdot \frac{1}{2},$$

$$k_1 = 1, \qquad\qquad k_3 = 1 \cdot \frac{2}{3}.$$

Show that

$$k_n = \frac{n-1}{n} \cdot k_{n-2}, \quad n = 2, 3, 4, \ldots$$

Exercise 3. Evaluate each of the following integrals:

(i) $\quad\quad\quad \int_a^b L, \; i.e., \int_a^b L \cdot I', \; (0 < a < b),$

(ii) $\quad\quad\quad \int_a^b \frac{I}{1 + I^2}, \; i.e., \frac{1}{2} \int_a^b \{L[1 + I^2]\}',$

(iii) $\quad\quad\quad \int_a^b A, \; i.e., \int_a^b A \cdot I',$

(iv) $\quad\quad\quad\quad\quad \int_a^b T,$

(v) $\quad\quad\quad\quad\quad \int_a^b K.$

The interval $[a,b]$ must be subject to restrictions in (i), (iv), and (v).

Exercise 4. Evaluate the integrals,

(i) $\quad\quad\quad\quad\quad \int_a^b K^3,$

(ii) $\quad\quad\quad\quad\quad \int_a^b T^3,$

(iii) $\quad\quad\quad\quad\quad \int_a^b L^2,$

(iv) $\quad\quad\quad\quad\quad \int_a^b IS.$

The interval $[a,b]$ must be restricted in some of these.

Examples. Since we see by inspection that

$$\frac{1}{(I + 1)(I + 2)} = \frac{1}{I + 1} - \frac{1}{I + 2},$$

then, for any interval not containing -1 or -2,

$$\int_a^b \frac{1}{(I + 1)(I + 2)} = \int_a^b \{L[|I + 1|] - L[|I + 2|]\}'.$$

Similarly,

$$\frac{1}{(I+1)(I+2)(I+3)} = \left\{ \frac{1}{I+1} - \frac{1}{I+2} \right\} \cdot \frac{1}{I+3} = \frac{1}{(I+1)(I+3)} - \frac{1}{(I+2)(I+3)}$$

$$= \frac{1}{2} \left\{ \frac{1}{I+1} - \frac{1}{I+3} \right\} - \left\{ \frac{1}{I+2} - \frac{1}{I+3} \right\} = \left\{ \frac{1}{2} L[\,|I+1|\,] + \frac{1}{2} L[\,|I+3|\,] - L[\,|I+2|\,] \right\}'.$$

Exercise 5. Evaluate the integral

$$\int_0^1 \frac{3I^2 + 1}{(I+1)^2 (I+2)(I+3)} \cdot$$

Note that

$$\frac{3I^2 + 1}{(I+1)^2 (I+2)(I+3)} = \frac{3(I^2 + 2I + 1) - 6(I+1) + 4}{(I+1)^2 (I+2)(I+3)}$$

$$= \frac{3}{(I+2)(I+3)} - \frac{6}{(I+1)(I+2)(I+3)} + \frac{4}{(I+1)^2 (I+2)(I+3)} \cdot$$

Exercise 6. Suppose $[a,b]$ is an interval not containing 0, -2, or 2, and evaluate the integral

$$\int_a^b \frac{1 + I^2}{I(I^2 - 4)} \cdot$$

Exercise 7. Show that $\int_0^1 \frac{1}{9I^2 - 16} = -\frac{L(7)}{24} \cdot$

Examples. To obtain a simple graph whose derivative is

$$\frac{1}{(1+I)^2 (1+I^2)} ,$$

consider,

$$\frac{1}{(1+I)^2 (1+I^2)} + \frac{aI + b}{1+I^2} = \frac{aI^3 + (2a+b)I^2 + (a+2b)I + (b+1)}{(1+I)^2 (1+I^2)} ,$$

where each of a and b is a number to be determined so that $I^2 + 1$ shall be a factor of the numerator of the fraction in the right hand member. We use "long division":

$$
\begin{array}{r}
aI + (2a+b) \\
I^2 + 1 \overline{\smash{\big)}\, aI^3 + (2a+b)I^2 + (a+2b)I + (b+1)} \\
\underline{aI^3 \qquad\qquad\qquad + \qquad aI} \\
(2a+b)I^2 + \qquad 2bI + (b+1) \\
\underline{(2a+b)I^2 \qquad\qquad + (2a+b)} \\
2bI + (1-2a)
\end{array}
$$

The remainder is 0 if $b = 0$ and $a = \dfrac{1}{2}$. We then have

$$\frac{1}{(1 + I^2)^2 (1 + I^2)} + \frac{\frac{1}{2}I}{1 + I^2} = \frac{\frac{1}{2}I + 1}{(1 + I)^2}$$

or

$$\frac{1}{(1 + I)^2(1 + I^2)} = -\frac{1}{4} \cdot \frac{2I}{1 + I^2} + \frac{1}{2} \cdot \frac{1}{1 + I} + \frac{1}{2} \cdot \frac{1}{(1 + I)^2}$$

$$= \left\{ -\frac{1}{4} L[1 + I^2] + \frac{1}{2} L[\,|1 + I|] - \frac{1}{2} \cdot \frac{1}{1 + I} \right\}'.$$

Exercise 8. Show that

$$\frac{1}{I^2 + I + 1} = \frac{1}{I^2 + I + \frac{1}{4} + \frac{3}{4}} = \frac{1}{\left(I + \frac{1}{2}\right)^2 + \frac{3}{4}} = \left\{ A\left[\frac{2I + 1}{\sqrt{3}}\right] \right\}' \cdot \frac{2}{\sqrt{3}}.$$

Hence find the integral from 0 to 1 of this simple graph.

Exercise 9. Evaluate the following integrals:

(i)
$$\int_a^b \frac{1}{I^2 + 4},$$

(ii)
$$\int_a^b \frac{1}{(I^2 + 1)(I^2 + I + 1)},$$

(iii)
$$\int_0^2 \frac{1}{I^3 + 1}.$$

A THEOREM ON TRANSFORMATION OF INTEGRALS

Theorem. Suppose that
(i) $[a,b]$ is an interval, g is a simple graph whose X-projection is the interval $[p,q]$ such that

$$g(p) = a \text{ and } g(q) = b,$$

the X-projection of g' is $[p,q]$ and g' has property (S) at each of its points;
(ii) f is a simple graph whose X-projection is the Y-projection $[r,s]$ of g and has property (S) at each of its points; and
(iii) h is the simple graph defined by

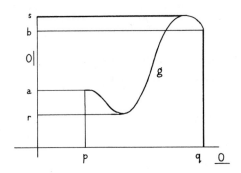

$$h(x) = \begin{cases} \int_a^x f, & \text{if } a < x \leq s, \\ 0, & \text{if } x = a, \\ -\int_x^a f, & \text{if } r \leq x < a, \end{cases}$$

so that $h' = f$. Then,

$$\int_a^b f = \int_a^b h' = \int_p^q \{h[g]\}' = \int_p^q h'[g] \cdot g' = \int_p^q f[g] \cdot g';$$

i.e.,

$$\int_a^b f = \int_p^q f[g] \cdot g'.$$

This result is almost indispensable in evaluating certain integrals.

Examples. $\int_0^1 \dfrac{1}{(1 + I^2)^2} = \int_0^{\pi/4} \dfrac{1}{(1 + T^2)^2} \cdot T' = \int_0^{\pi/4} \dfrac{1}{(K^4)} \cdot K^2$

$$= \int_0^{\pi/4} C^2 = \int_0^{\pi/4} \left\{ \dfrac{CS + I}{2} \right\}' = \dfrac{1}{4}\left(1 + \dfrac{\pi}{4}\right).$$

The area of the region $[Q[1 - I^2];0,1]$, which is one fourth the area of a circular disc of radius 1, is

$$\int_0^1 Q[1 - I^2] = \int_0^{\pi/2} Q[1 - S^2] \cdot S' = \int_0^{\pi/2} C^2 = \int_0^{\pi/2} \left\{\dfrac{CS + I}{2}\right\}' = \dfrac{\pi}{4}.$$

Hence the area of a circular disc of radius 1 is π.

Exercise 10. Suppose r is a positive number and find the area of one fourth the circular disc of radius r:

$$\int_0^r Q[r^2 - I^2].$$

Exercise 11. If k is a number between 0 and 1,

$$\int_0^{\pi/2} \frac{1}{1 - kS} = \int_0^1 \frac{1}{1 - kS[2A]} \cdot 2A'.$$

Evaluate this integral.

Exercise 12. Evaluate the integral $\int_0^{\pi/2} \dfrac{C}{S + C + 1}$.

Exercise 13. Evaluate each of the following integrals.

(i) $$\int_0^1 Q[4 + 9I^2],$$

(ii) $$\int_0^3 \frac{I}{Q[1 + I]} ,$$

(iii) $$\int_{-2}^{-1} Q[I^2 - 1],$$

and (iv) $$\int_0^1 \frac{1}{2 + Q} .$$

Problem. Try to invent a definition of *length* of a simple graph.

Computation Formulas Obtained by Means of the Integral

The approximation formulas for L and A were obtained by experimentation and conjecture. The integral furnishes a method for obtaining such formulas for many simple graphs.

We need a few preliminaries. First, it is convenient to make the following agreement:

$$\int_a^a f = 0 \text{ and } \int_b^a f = -\int_a^b f.$$

With this agreement, $L(x) = \int_1^x \frac{1}{I}$ for every positive number x, and $A(x) = \int_0^x \Omega$ for every number x. Second, the following lemma, which we leave for the reader to prove, will be useful:

Lemma. Suppose each of f and g is a simple graph with X-projection the interval $[a,b]$ having property (S) at each of its points and $g(x) \geq 0$ for every number x in $[a,b]$ or $g(x) \leq 0$ for every number x in $[a,b]$. Then, there exists a number c in the interval $[a,b]$ such that

$$\int_a^b fg = f(c) \cdot \int_a^b g.$$

COMPUTATION FORMULAS FOR L, A

We begin by rederiving the formulas for $L(c)$ found previously. If $c > 0$,

$$L(c) = \int_1^c H = \int_1^c H \cdot (I - k)',$$

where k is any number. Hence,

$$L(c) = \int_1^c \{H \cdot (I - k)\}' - \int_1^c (I - k) \cdot H' = \frac{c - k}{c} - (1 - k) + \int_1^c \frac{I - k}{I^2}.$$

The simplest formulas result if we take k to be 1 or c:

$$L(c) = \frac{c - 1}{c} + \int_1^c \frac{I - 1}{I^2}$$

and

$$L(c) = (c - 1) + \int_1^c \frac{I - c}{I^2}.$$

The first may be written,

$$L(c) = \frac{c - 1}{c} + \int_1^c I \cdot \left\{ \frac{1}{2}\left(\frac{I - 1}{I}\right)^2 \right\}'$$

so that, if $c \neq 1$, it follows from the Lemma that

$$L(c) = \frac{c - 1}{c} + \frac{1}{2}\left(\frac{c - 1}{c}\right)^2 \cdot c',$$

where c' is in the interval $[c,1]$ if $0 < c < 1$ and in the interval $[1,c]$ if $1 < c$.

To obtain a better approximation, we write,

$$L(c) = \frac{c - 1}{c} + \int_1^c \left(\frac{1}{I}\right)^2 \cdot \left\{ \frac{(I - 1)^2}{2} \right\}'$$

$$= \frac{c - 1}{c} + \int_1^c \left\{ \left(\frac{1}{I}\right)^2 \cdot \frac{(I - 1)^2}{2} \right\}' - \int_1^c \frac{(I - 1)^2}{2} \cdot \left\{ \left(\frac{1}{I}\right)^2 \right\}'$$

$$= \frac{c - 1}{c} + \frac{1}{2}\left(\frac{c - 1}{c}\right)^2 + \int_1^c I \cdot \left\{ \frac{1}{3}\left(\frac{I - 1}{I}\right)^3 \right\}'$$

$$= \frac{c - 1}{c} + \frac{1}{2}\left(\frac{c - 1}{c}\right)^2 + \frac{1}{3}\left(\frac{c - 1}{c}\right)^3 \cdot c',$$

where $c' = 1$, $c' = c$, or c' is a number between 1 and c.

Next, we write,

$$L(c) = \frac{c - 1}{c} + \frac{1}{2}\left(\frac{c - 1}{2}\right)^2 + \int_1^c \left(\frac{1}{I}\right)^3 \cdot \left\{ \frac{(I - 1)^3}{3} \right\}'$$

$$= \frac{c - 1}{c} + \frac{1}{2}\left(\frac{c - 1}{c}\right)^2 + \frac{1}{3}\left(\frac{c - 1}{c}\right)^3 + \int_1^c I \cdot \left\{ \frac{1}{4}\left(\frac{I - 1}{I}\right)^4 \right\}'$$

$$= \frac{c - 1}{c} + \frac{1}{2}\left(\frac{c - 1}{c}\right)^2 + \frac{1}{3}\left(\frac{c - 1}{c}\right)^3 + \frac{1}{4}\left(\frac{c - 1}{c}\right)^4 \cdot c', \quad 1 \lesseqgtr c' \lesseqgtr c,$$

and so on.

Exercise. Follow up the case $k = c$ and obtain the formulas,

$$L(c) = (c - 1) + \int_1^c \left(\frac{1}{I}\right)^2 \cdot \left\{\frac{(I - c)^2}{2}\right\}' = (c - 1) - \frac{1}{2}(c - 1)^2 \cdot \left(\frac{1}{c'}\right)^2,$$

where $c' = c$, $c' = 1$, or c' is a number between c and 1;

$$L(c) = (c - 1) - \frac{1}{2}(c - 1)^2 + \frac{1}{3}(c - 1)^3 \left(\frac{1}{c'}\right)^3,$$

and so on.

Obtain the approximation formulas for A by this process, starting with

$$A(c) = \int_0^c \frac{1}{1 + I^2} \cdot (I - k)'.$$

COMPUTATION FORMULAS FOR E, $\mathcal{S}$, $\mathcal{C}$

If c is a number,

$$E(c) = 1 + \int_0^c E' = 1 + \int_0^c E = 1 + \int_0^c E \cdot (I - k)',$$

where k is any number. Hence,

$$E(c) = 1 + \int_0^c \{E \cdot (I - k)\}' - \int_0^c (I - k) \cdot E'$$

$$= 1 + E(c) \cdot (c - k) - E(0) \cdot (-k) - \int_0^c (I - k) \cdot E.$$

Taking k to be c, we then have

$$E(c) = 1 + c - \int_0^c E \cdot \left\{\frac{(I - c)^2}{2}\right\}' = 1 + c + \frac{c^2}{2} \cdot E(c'),$$

where c' is 0, c, or a number between 0 and c.

Exercise. Show that, if c is a number and n a positive integer, there exists a number c' such that $0 \le c' \le c$ or $c \le c' \le 0$ and

$$E(c) = 1 + \frac{c}{1} + \frac{c^2}{1 \cdot 2} + \ldots + \frac{c^n}{1 \cdot 2 \cdot \ldots \cdot n} + \frac{c^{n+1}}{1 \cdot 2 \cdot \ldots \cdot (n+1)} \cdot E(c').$$

In case $n = 0$ this formula may be correctly interpreted to mean

$$E(c) = 1 + c \cdot E(c').$$

In particular, $E(1) = e = 2.718281828$, to nine decimal places. Show that, if c is a number and n a positive integer, there exists a number c' such that $c \leq c' \leq 0$ or $0 \leq c' \leq c$ and

$$S(c) = c + \frac{c^3}{1 \cdot 2 \cdot 3} + \cdots + \frac{c^{2n-1}}{1 \cdot 2 \cdot \ldots \cdot (2n-1)} + \frac{c^{2n+1}}{1 \cdot 2 \cdot \ldots \cdot (2n+1)} \cdot \mathcal{C}(c').$$

Obtain the analogous formula for $\mathcal{C}$.

Exercise

(i) Show that, if n is a positive integer and h a positive number, there exists a vertical line $k|$ such that every point of the simple graph $\dfrac{E}{(I^n)}$ to the right of $k|$ is above h.

(ii) Show that, if a is a positive number and b a positive number,

$$(1 + a)(1 + b) < E(a + b) \text{ and } (1 - \frac{a}{1+a})(1 - \frac{b}{1+b}) > \frac{1}{E(a+b)}.$$

(iii) Show that, if c is a positive number, there exists a positive number d such that, if x is a number distinct from 0 which differs from 0 by less than d, then $(1 + x)^{1/x}$ differs from e by less than c.

THE BINOMIAL THEOREM

Theorem. If m is a number and c a number distinct from 0 and greater than -1 and n a positive integer, there exists a number c' such that $c \leq c' \leq 0$ or $0 \leq c' \leq c$ and

$$(1 + c)^m = 1 + \int_{/0}^{c} \{(1 + I)^m\}' = 1 + \frac{m}{1}c + \frac{m(m-1)}{1 \cdot 2}c^2 + \cdots$$

$$+ \frac{m(m-1)\ldots(m-n+1)}{1 \cdot 2 \cdot \ldots \cdot n}c^n + \frac{m(m-1)\ldots(m-n)}{1 \cdot 2 \cdot \ldots \cdot (n+1)}c^{n+1} \cdot \frac{(1+c')^{m+1}}{1+c}.$$

In case $n = 0$, this formula may be correctly interpreted to mean

$$(1 + c)^m = 1 + \frac{m}{1}c \cdot \frac{(1+c')^{m+1}}{1+c}.$$

Note that:

$$0 < \frac{(1+c')^{m+1}}{1+c} \leq \begin{cases} (1+c)^m & \text{if } c > 0,\ m+1 > 0 \text{ or } c < 0,\ m+1 < 0, \\ \dfrac{1}{1+c} & \text{if } c < 0,\ m+1 < 0 \text{ or } c < 0,\ m+1 > 0. \end{cases}$$

Example. To use this "binomial theorem" to compute approximations to $\sqrt{2}$, we first write 2 as a fraction such as $\dfrac{50}{25}$ or $\dfrac{98}{49}$ in which the denominator is the square of a positive integer and the numerator "near" the square of a positive integer. Taking the first, we then have:

$$\sqrt{2} = \frac{1}{5}(7^2 + 1)^{1/2} = \frac{7}{5}\left(1 + \left[\frac{1}{7}\right]^2\right)^{1/2} = \frac{7}{5}\left[1 + \frac{1}{2}\left(\frac{1}{7}\right)^2 - \frac{1}{8}\left(\frac{1}{7}\right)^4 + \frac{1}{16}\left(\frac{1}{7}\right)^6\right] + R,$$

where $|R| < .00000003$.

Exercise

(i) Compute $2^{1/3}$ correct to six decimal places.

(ii) Suppose k is a positive number less than 1. Find approximation formulas for $\int_0^{\pi/2} (1 - k^2 s^2)^{1/2}$.

(iii) Show that, if n is a positive integer,

$$\left(1 + \frac{1}{2} + \frac{1}{3} + \ldots + \frac{1}{n}\right) - L(n + 1) < \frac{5}{8}.$$

LENGTH OF A SIMPLE GRAPH

The *inner product* of the point (x,y), denoted by P, and the point (u,v), denoted by Q, is the number $xu + yv$:

$$((P,Q)) = xu + yv.$$

The *sum* P + Q of P and Q is the point $(x + u, y + v)$; and, if k is a number, the product $k \cdot P$ is the point (kx, ky):

$$P + Q = (x + u, y + v)$$

and

$$k \cdot P = (kx, ky).$$

Suppose each of P, Q, and R is a point. The inner product has the following properties:

(i) $((P,Q))$ is a number and $((P,P))$ is a positive number unless P = (0,0),

(ii) $((P + Q, R)) = ((P,R)) + ((Q,R))$,

(iii) $((P,Q)) = ((Q,P))$,

and, if k is a number,

(iv) $((k \cdot P, Q)) = k((P,Q))$.

As a consequence of these properties, we have:

(v) $((P,Q))^2 \leq ((P,P))((Q,Q))$.

If P is the point (x,y), the *negative* of P is $(-1) \cdot P$; *i.e.*,

$$-P = (-x,-y).$$

The *difference* P - Q is the point P + (-Q).

Definition. If P is a point and Q a point, the *distance* from P to Q is the number

$$((P - Q, P - Q))^{1/2},$$

and is denoted by $|P - Q|$.

The distance from P to Q is a positive number unless P = Q, and the distance from P to Q is the distance from Q to P. The distance from (x, y) to $(0, 0)$ is $(x^2 + y^2)^{1/2}$, as previously defined; and the distance from the point $(a, 0)$ to the point $(b, 0)$ is, if $a < b$, the number $b - a$, which is the same as the length of the interval $[a, b]$. Distance has the following property:

(vi) $|P - R| \leq |P - Q| + |Q - R|$,

called the *triangle property*.

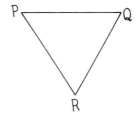

With these preliminaries, we are now prepared to define the length of a simple graph.

Definition. The statement that the simple graph f has *length* on the interval $[a, b]$ means that the X-projection of f includes $[a, b]$ and there exists a number k such that, if D is a finite collection of non-overlapping intervals filling up $[a, b]$, then the sum of all the distances

$$|(r, f(r)) - (s, f(s))|,$$

taken for all the intervals $[r, s]$ in D, does not exceed k. If f has length on $[a, b]$, the *least* such number k is called the *length* of f on $[a, b]$ and is denoted by

$$\ell_a^b \, f.$$

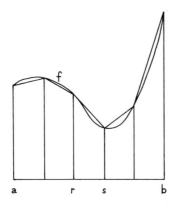

Theorem. Suppose f is a simple graph whose X-projection includes the interval $[a,b]$. The following statements are true.

(i) If f has length on $[a,b]$, and c is a number between a and b, then f has length on $[a,c]$ and on $[c,b]$ and

$$\ell_a^b f = \ell_a^c f + \ell_c^b f.$$

(ii) If the derivative f' of f is such that $Q[1 + (f')^2]$ is integrable on $[a,b]$, then

$$\ell_a^b f = \int_a^b Q[1 + (f')^2].$$

Exercise
(i) Find the length on $[0,1]$ of I^2.
(ii) Find the length on $[1,2]$ of L.
(iii) Show that $\ell_0^{\pi/2} S = \sqrt{2} \int_0^{\pi/2} (1 - k^2 S^2)^{1/2}$, where $k = \dfrac{\sqrt{2}}{2}$, and find an approximation to this number correct to four decimal places.

Theorem. If f is a simple graph whose derivative f' has X-projection $[a,b]$ and property (S) at each of its points, and s is the simple graph defined by

$$s(x) = \begin{cases} 0, & \text{if } x = a, \\ \ell_a^x f, & \text{if } a < x \le b, \end{cases}$$

then, if $[u,v]$ is a subinterval of $[a,b]$,

$$\{s'(u) \cdot (v - u)\}^2 = \{v - u\}^2 + \{f'(u) \cdot (v - u)\}^2,$$

71

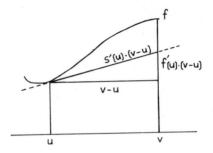

so that $s'(u) \cdot (v - u)$ is the length on $[u,v]$ of the straight line tangent to f at the point $(u, f(u))$.(See figure.)

LENGTH OF AN ARC OF A CIRCLE

The statement that M is the circle with center the point c and radius the positive number r means that M is the point set to which P belongs only if P is a point whose distance from c is r: $|P - c| = r$. In particular, the circle with center $(0,0)$ and radius r is the set of all points P such that $|P| = r$. The upper half of this circle is the simple graph $Q[r^2 - I^2]$, which we denote by q.

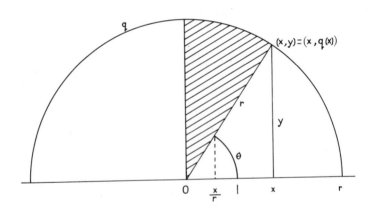

Exercise. Suppose x is a positive number less than r.

(i) q has length $r \cdot B(x/r)$ on $[0,x]$ and length $\ell_0^y q$ on $[x,r]$, where $y = q(x)$.

72

(ii) The only positive number x less than r such that $x = q(x)$ is the number $\dfrac{r\sqrt{2}}{2}$, which we denote by c. Then,

$$\ell_0^r \, q = \ell_0^c \, q + \ell_c^r \, q = \ell_0^c \, q + \ell_0^c \, q = 2r \cdot B\left(\frac{\sqrt{2}}{2}\right) = r \cdot \frac{\pi}{2}\,.$$

If, in particular, $r = 1$, the length of the quarter circle is $\dfrac{\pi}{2}$.

(iii) Suppose the number θ is defined by

$$r \cdot \theta = \ell_x^r \, q.$$

Then,

$$\theta = \frac{\pi}{2} - B\left(\frac{x}{r}\right) = \ell_{\frac{x}{r}}^1 \, Q[1 - I^2\,],$$

$$C(\theta) = \frac{x}{r} \text{ and } S(\theta) = \frac{y}{r}\,.$$

The number θ is the *argument* of the point (x,y), previously defined, and is the length on $[x/r, 1]$ of $Q[1 - I^2\,]$, $(x^2 + y^2 = r^2)$.

Exercise

(i) The area of the shaded region in the preceding figure is $(1/2)r \cdot r \cdot (\pi/2 - \theta)$; *i.e.*, one-half the product of the radius of the circle times the length of q on $[0, x]$.

(ii) Suppose R is a number greater than r. Show that the area of the shaded region in the next figure is

$$\frac{R + r}{2} \cdot \theta \cdot (R - r);$$

i.e., the product of the length of the arc h (See figure) times the difference R - r of the radii of the two circles.

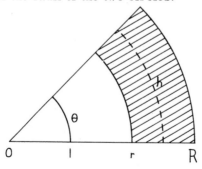

POLAR EQUATIONS

If (x,y) is a point, any ordered number pair (r,θ) such that $x = rC(\theta)$ and $y = rS(\theta)$ is said to be a pair of polar coordinates of the point (x,y). If f is a simple graph, the point set M to which (x,y) belongs only if there is a point (r,θ) of f such that (r,θ) is a pair of polar coordinates of (x,y) is called the graph of the polar equation $r = f(\theta)$.

Example. The circle with center $(1,0)$ and radius 1 is the graph of the polar equation $r = 2C(\theta)$. (See figure).

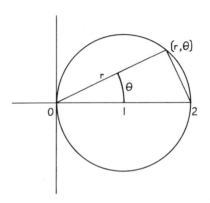

Exercise
Sketch the graph of each of the following polar equations:

  (i) $r = 4C(2\theta)$,
  (ii) $r = 2\{1 - S(\theta)\}$,
  (iii) $r = 1 + 2S(\theta)$.

The simple graph f shown in the next figure is the part of the graph of the polar equation $r = 2 \cdot C(2\theta)$ for which $0 \le \theta \le \frac{\pi}{4}$. The area of the region $[f;0,2]$ may be found as follows.

Let $[\theta_{i-1}, \theta_i]$, $i = 1, 2, \ldots, n$, be a finite collection of nonoverlapping intervals filling up $[0, \frac{\pi}{4}]$ and $r_i = 2C(2\theta_i)$. The sum

$$\sum_{i=1}^{n} \tfrac{1}{2} r_i^2 (\theta_i - \theta_{i-1}) = \sum_{i=1}^{n} 2C^2(2\theta_i)(\theta_i - \theta_{i-1})$$

is the sum of the areas of n regions of which the one shaded in the figure is typical. If the area of the region $[f;0,2]$ is the least number which no such sum exceeds, then the area is the integral

$$\int_0^{\pi/4} 2C^2\,[2I] = \int_0^{\pi/2} C^2 = \int_0^{\pi/2} \left\{\frac{I + CS}{2}\right\}' = \frac{\pi}{4}\,.$$

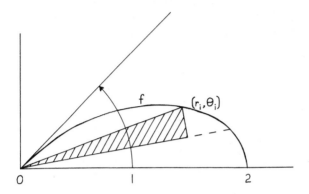

Exercise. Find the area of the region bounded below by $\underline{0}$ and bounded above by the part of the graph of the polar equation $r = 2\{1 - C(\theta)\}$ for which $0 \le \theta \le \pi$.

ANALOGY BETWEEN S, $\mathcal{C}$ AND S, C

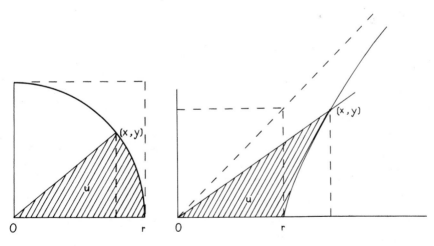

Suppose r is a positive number. The area u of the region shaded in the first of the preceding figures is $\frac{1}{2}xy + \int_x^r Q[r^2 - I^2]$. If $\theta = \frac{2u}{(r^2)}$, then $C(\theta) = \frac{x}{r}$ and $S(\theta) = \frac{y}{r}$. Now, the area u of the region shaded in the second figure is $\frac{1}{2}xy - \int_r^x Q[I^2 - r^2]$. If $\theta = \frac{2u}{(r^2)}$, then $\mathcal{C}(\theta) = \frac{x}{r}$ and $\mathcal{S}(\theta) = \frac{y}{r}$.

Simple Graphs Made to Order

We consider here the problem of constructing simple graphs, mainly as combinations of I, E, S, and C, which have certain prescribed properties.

THE EQUATION $f' = g \cdot f + h$

If each of g and h is a simple graph whose X-projection is the set of all numbers having property (S) at each of its points and if (a,b) is a point, does there exist a simple graph f containing (a,b) such that $f' = g \cdot f + h$?

The simple graph E has the property that $E' = E$. Let us try to construct f out of E:

$$f = v\mathrm{E}[u] .$$

Since $f' = v\mathrm{E}[u]u' + v'\mathrm{E}[u]$, we require that

(i) $$v\mathrm{E}[u]u' + v'\mathrm{E}[u] = g \cdot v\mathrm{E}[u] + h$$

and

(ii) $$v(a)\mathrm{E}(u(a)) = b .$$

Now, (i) is true if $u' = g$ and $v' = h\mathrm{E}[-u]$ which, along with (ii), are true if

$$u(x) = \int_a^x g \quad \text{and} \quad v(x) = b + \int_a^x h\mathrm{E}[-u].$$

Therefore, one simple graph f satisfying the given conditions is given by

$$f(x) = b\mathrm{E}\,(u(x)) + \int_a^x h\mathrm{E}[u(x)-u],$$

where

$$u(x) = \int_a^{x\cdot} g.$$

Suppose there is another, F, and consider the difference $w = \mathrm{F} - f$. Then, $w(a) = 0$ and $w' = gw$. The quotient $\dfrac{w}{\mathrm{E}\,[u]}$ has slope 0 at each of its points and is therefore a horizontal line $\underline{k}$:

$$w = k\mathrm{E}[u].$$

Since $w(a) = 0$, then $k = 0$ and $w = 0$; *i.e.*, $\mathrm{F} = f$. *The problem has only one solution.*

Exercise. Show, in contrast, that there are many simple graphs f such that $f(0) = 0$ and $f' = 2\mathrm{Q}[f]$. One is $\underline{0}$. Find another.

THE EQUATION $f'' + kf = g$

If k is a number, g a simple graph whose X-projection is the set of all numbers having property (S) at each of its points, (a,b) a point, and m a number, does there exist a simple graph f containing (a,b) with slope m at this point such that $f'' + kf = g$?

Case 1. $k = 0$. There are two simple graphs α and β such that $\alpha'' = \underline{0}$, $\beta'' = \underline{0}$ and

$$\alpha(a) = 1, \quad \alpha'(a) = 0,$$
$$\beta(a) = 0, \quad \beta'(a) = 1,$$

namely: $\alpha = \underline{1}$ and $\beta = \mathrm{I} - a$. We try to construct the solution f in the form

$$f = u\alpha + v\beta.$$

Since $f(a) = b$, we see that it is necessary to have

$$u(a) = b.$$

Now, $f' = u\alpha' + \alpha u' + v\beta' + \beta v'$. Since f'' is involved, about the only way we can expect this to work is to have

$$\alpha u' + \beta v' = \underline{0},$$

$$f' = u\alpha' + v\beta', \quad v(a) = m.$$

Then, $f'' = u\alpha'' + v\beta'' + u'\alpha' + v'\beta' = v'$, so that we require

$$v' = g.$$

We have to determine u and v from the equations,

$$u' + (I - a) \cdot v' = \underline{0},$$
$$v' = g,$$
$$u(a) = b \text{ and } v(a) = m.$$

Thus, $u' = -(I - a) \cdot g$, $v' = g$,

$$u(x) = b - \int_a^x (I - a) \cdot g, \quad v(x) = m + \int_a^x g,$$

and

$$f(x) = b + m \cdot (x - a) + \int_a^x (x - I) \cdot g.$$

This is the only simple graph with the prescribed properties.

Case 2. $k < 0$. In this case we suppose $k = -r^2$ where r is a positive number. There are two simple graphs α and β such that $\alpha'' - r^2 \alpha = \underline{0}$, $\beta'' - r^2 \beta = \underline{0}$ and

$$\alpha(a) = 1, \qquad \alpha'(a) = 0,$$
$$\beta(a) = 0, \qquad \beta'(a) = 1,$$

namely: $\alpha = \mathcal{C}[r(I - a)]$ and $r\beta = \mathbf{S}[r(I - a)]$. We try to construct the solution f in the form

$$f = u\alpha + v\beta.$$

This can be done, and we obtain

$$f(x) = b\mathcal{C}(r(x - a)) + \frac{m}{r}\mathbf{S}(r(x - a)) + \frac{1}{r}\int_a^x \mathbf{S}[r(x - I)] \cdot g.$$

Case 3. $k > 0$. In this case we suppose $k = r^2$, $r > 0$. In this case, $\alpha = C[r(I - a)]$ and $r\beta = S[r(I - a)]$, we try to obtain f in the form $f = u\alpha + v\beta$, and we find

$$f(x) = bC(r(x - a)) + \frac{m}{r}S(r(x - a)) + \frac{1}{r}\int_a^x S[r(x - I)] \cdot g.$$

THE EQUATION $f'' + \underline{p}f' + \underline{q}f = g$

The problem of obtaining a simple graph f whose X-projection is the set of all numbers containing the point (a,b) and having slope m at this point such that $f'' + pf' + qf = g$, can be reduced to the problems already discussed. It is understood that each of p and q is a number and g a simple graph whose X-projection is the set of all numbers having property (S) at each of its points. Trying simplest things first, we try

$$f = u\mathrm{E}[k\mathrm{I}],$$

where k is a number. Then

$$f' = ku\mathrm{E}[k\mathrm{I}] + u'\mathrm{E}[k\mathrm{I}],$$

$$f'' = k^2 u\mathrm{E}[k\mathrm{I}] + 2ku'\mathrm{E}[k\mathrm{I}] + u''\mathrm{E}[k\mathrm{I}],$$

and $f'' + pf' + qf = \mathrm{E}[k\mathrm{I}]\{u'' + (2k+p)u' + (k^2 + kp + q)u\}.$

If we choose k to be $-\dfrac{p}{2}$, our problem is reduced to the problem of finding a simple graph u for which

$$u'' + \frac{4q - p^2}{4} u = \mathrm{E}[-\frac{p}{2}\mathrm{I}] \cdot g.$$

Exercise.   In each of the following cases, find a simple graph f containing the point (a,b) with slope m at this point and satisfying the stated equation:

  (i) $f'' + 2f' + f = g$,
  (ii) $f'' - 2f' + 2f = g$,
  (iii) $f'' + 2f' + 10f = g$.

Here g is a simple graph with X-projection the set of all numbers having property (S) at each of its points.

More about Integrals

The integral as developed in the preceding chapters is rather closely tied to the derivative. For example, to express a simple graph f as an integral by the formula $f(x) = f(a) + \int_a^x f'$ requires that f' be integrable on the interval over which the integral is extended. To find a more general kind of integral, we begin by generalizing the notion of length of an interval.

g - LENGTH OF AN INTERVAL

Definition. The statement that $g\big|_a^b$ is the g-*length* of the interval $[a,b]$ means that g is a simple graph whose X-projection includes $[a,b]$ and

$$g\big|_a^b = g(b) - g(a).$$

In particular, the I-*length* of $[a,b]$ is $b - a$, the ordinary length of $[a,b]$.

Suppose that W is a metal wire of length c, measured in centimeters, that P_0 denotes one end of W, and that, if x is a positive number not greater than c, P_x denotes the place on W a distance x from P_0. Let g be the simple graph whose X-projection is $[0,c]$ defined by

$$g(x) = \begin{cases} 0, & \text{if } x = 0, \\ \text{the mass, measured in} & \\ \text{grams, of the piece of} & \\ \text{W from } P_0 \text{ to } P_x, & \text{if } 0 < x \le c. \end{cases}$$

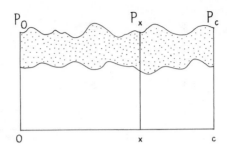

Then, the g-length of the subinterval $[a,b]$ of $[0,c]$ is the mass of that piece of W from P_a to P_b.

As another illustration, let P_0 be a place above the surface of the earth and c the time, measured in seconds, required for a falling body to pass from P_0 to the place P_c on the earth. For each number t in $[0,c]$, P_t denotes the place occupied by the body at time t. Let f denote the simple graph such that

$$f(t) = \begin{cases} 0, & \text{if } t = 0, \\ \text{the distance, measured in feet,} \\ \text{from } P_0 \text{ to } P_t & \text{if } 0 < t \le c. \end{cases}$$

The f-length of the subinterval $[a,b]$ of $[0,c]$ is the distance from P_a to P_b.

g-length has the fundamental property that, if c is a number between a and b, then

$$g\Big|_a^b = g\Big|_a^c + g\Big|_c^b .$$

In case g' has X-projection $[a,b]$, the g-length of $[a,b]$ is expressible in terms of ordinary length by the formula:

$$g\Big|_a^b = g'(c) \cdot I\Big|_a^b ,$$

where c is some number between a and b.

The statement that the simple graph g is *nondecreasing* on the interval $[a,b]$ means that, if $[p,q]$ is a subinterval of $[a,b]$, $g\Big|_p^q \ge 0$; *i.e.*, the point of g with abscissa p is not higher than the point of g with abscissa q. The simple graphs of the preceding illustrations are nondecreasing.

INTEGRAL OF A SIMPLE GRAPH WITH RESPECT TO A SIMPLE GRAPH

We suppose, to begin with, that the simple graph f is bounded on the interval $[a,b]$ and the simple graph g is nondecreasing on $[a,b]$.

The statement that $_iS$ is an inner sum for f with respect to g on $[a,b]$ means that there exists a finite collection D of nonoverlapping intervals filling up $[a,b]$ such that, if the g-length of each interval in D is multiplied by the largest number k which exceeds the ordinate of no point of f whose abscissa is in that interval, then the sum of all the products so formed is $_iS$. This is a generalization of inner sum for f with respect to I on $[a,b]$ used previously. The outer sum $_oS$ of f with respect to g on $[a,b]$ is the analogous generalization of outer sum used previously.

If V is the largest number which exceeds the ordinate of no point of f whose abscissa is in $[a,b]$ and if U is the smallest number exceeded by the ordinate of no point of f whose abscissa is in $[a,b]$, and if $_iS$ and $_oS$ are an inner and outer sum for f with respect to g on $[a,b]$, then

$$\mathrm{V} \cdot g\Big|_a^b \leq \,_iS \leq \,_oS \leq \mathrm{U} \cdot g\Big|_a^b .$$

This is trivial in case $_iS$ and $_oS$ are based on the *same* collection D of nonoverlapping intervals filling up $[a,b]$.

The smallest number which no inner sum for f with respect to g on $[a,b]$ exceeds is called the inner integral of f with respect to g on $[a,b]$ and is denoted by

$$_i\!\int_a^b f \, dg.$$

The largest number which exceeds no outer sum for f with respect to g on $[a,b]$ is called the outer integral of f with respect to g on $[a,b]$ and is denoted by

$$_o\!\int_a^b f \, dg.$$

Note. In both these symbols, the letter d stands for the phrase "with respect to."

There is the following inequality:

$$\mathrm{V} \cdot g\Big|_a^b \leq \,_iS \leq \,_i\!\int_a^b f \, dg \leq \,_o\!\int_a^b f \, dg \leq \,_oS \leq \mathrm{U} \cdot g\Big|_a^b .$$

Theorem. If the simple graph f is bounded on the interval $[a,b]$ and the simple graph g is nondecreasing on $[a,b]$, then each two of the following four statements are equivalent.

(i) $_i\int_a^b f\,dg = {_o}\int_a^b f\,dg.$

(ii) If c is a positive number, there exists an inner sum $_iS$ and an outer sum $_oS$ such that $_oS - {_i}S < c.$

(iii) If each of c and d is a positive number, there exists a finite collection D of nonoverlapping intervals filling up $[a,b]$ such that, if there is an interval of D containing two numbers x and y such that $f(x)$ and $f(y)$ differ by more than c, then the sum of the g-lengths of all such intervals of D is less than d.

(iv) There exists a number J such that, if c is a positive number, there is a finite collection D of nonoverlapping intervals filling up $[a,b]$ such that, if D$'$ is a finite collection of nonoverlapping intervals filling up $[a,b]$, with each end of each interval of D an end of an interval of D$'$, and the g-length of each interval of D$'$ is multiplied by the ordinate of any point of f whose abscissa is in that interval, then the sum of all the products so formed differs from J by less than c.

Among these four mutually equivalent statements, there is one which does not make explicit use of the conditions imposed upon f and g. We accordingly take this statement, (iv), as our definition of integrability in the general case.

Definition. The statement that the simple graph f is integrable on $[a,b]$ with respect to the simple graph g means that each of f and g has X-projection including $[a,b]$ and that there exists a number J such that, if c is a positive number, there is a finite collection D of nonoverlapping intervals filling up $[a,b]$ such that, if D$'$ is a finite collection of nonoverlapping intervals filling up $[a,b]$, with each end of each interval of D an end of an interval of D$'$, and the g-length of each interval in D$'$ is multiplied by the ordinate of any point of f whose abscissa is in that interval, then the sum of all the products so formed differs from J by less than c. If f is integrable on $[a,b]$ with respect to g, the number J of the preceding statement is called the integral from a to b of f with respect to g and is denoted by

$$\int_a^b f\,dg.$$

The integral introduced in the earlier chapters is $\int_a^b f\, d\mathrm{I}$. We shall continue to write $\int_a^b f$ for this integral.

PROPERTIES OF $\int_a^b f\, dg$

It should be emphasized that, if f is bounded and g nondecreasing on $[a,b]$, then any one of the four mutually equivalent statements in the preceding theorem may be taken as definition of the statement f is integrable with respect to g ("g-integrable") on $[a,b]$.

If the simple graph g has X-projection which includes the interval $[a,b]$ and if k is a number, then $\underline{k}$ is g-integrable on $[a,b]$ and

$$\int_a^b \underline{k}\, dg = k \cdot g \big|_a^b .$$

In particular, if $a < x \le b$,

$$g(x) = g(a) + \int_a^x \underline{1}\, dg.$$

We agree that $\int_a^a f\, dg = 0$ (and $\int_b^a f\, dg = - \int_a^b f\, dg$). Then, $g(x) = g(a) + \int_a^x \underline{1}\, dg$ for every number x in $[a,b]$.

If f is g-integrable on $[a,b]$ and fg' is I-integrable on $[a,b]$, then

$$\int_a^b f\, dg = \int_a^b fg' .$$

In particular, if g' is I-integrable on $[a,b]$,

$$\int_a^b \underline{1}\, dg = g(b) - g(a) = \int_a^b g' .$$

If f is g-integrable on $[a,b]$ then g is f-integrable on $[a,b]$ and

$$\int_a^b f\, dg = (fg)\big|_a^b - \int_a^b g\, df.$$

If f is g-integrable on $[a,b]$ and k is a number, then

$$\int_a^b kf\, dg = \int_a^b f\, d(kg) = k \int_a^b f\, dg$$

and

$$\int_a^b f\,d(g+k) = \int_a^b f\,dg.$$

If each of f_1 and f_2 is g_1-integrable on $[a,b]$ and g_2-integrable on $[a,b]$, then

$$\int_a^b (f_1+f_2)\,d(g_1+g_2) = \int_a^b f_1\,dg_1 + \int_a^b f_1\,dg_2 + \int_a^b f_2\,dg_1 + \int_a^b f_2\,dg_2.$$

Theorem. If f is g-integrable on $[a,b]$, then there exists a finite collection D of nonoverlapping intervals filling up $[a,b]$ such that, if $[p,q]$ is an interval of D on which f is unbounded, $g(x)=g(p)$ for each number x in $[p,q]$; *i.e.*, g *is constant on* $[p,q]$.

We abbreviate the sum of products described in the definition of integrability as

$$\sum\nolimits_{D'} f(x) \cdot g \big|_p^q \ ,$$

which is the sum of the g-length of $[p,q]$ times the ordinate of the point of f whose abscissa is the number x of $[p,q]$, taken for all $[p,q]$ in D$'$.

Theorem. Suppose each of f and g is a simple graph whose X-projection includes the interval $[a,b]$. The following two statements are equivalent:

(i) f is g-integrable on $[a,b]$

and

(ii) if c is a positive number, there exists a finite collection D of nonoverlapping intervals filling up $[a,b]$ such that, if D$'$ is a finite collection of nonoverlapping intervals filling up $[a,b]$ with each end of each interval of D an end of an interval of D$'$, then

$$\left| \sum\nolimits_{D'} f(x) \cdot g\big|_p^q - \sum\nolimits_{D} f(y) \cdot g\big|_r^s \right| < c.$$

Corollary. If f is g-integrable on $[a,b]$ and if c is a number between a and b, then f is g-integrable on $[a,c]$ and on $[c,b]$ and $\int_a^b f\,dg = \int_a^c f\,dg + \int_c^b f\,dg.$

Problem. Investigate conditions under which:

$$\int_a^b f\,d\mathrm{F} = \int_a^b fg\,dh,$$

where

$$F(x) = \int_a^x g \, dh.$$

BOUNDED VARIATION

The statement that the simple graph g is of bounded variation on the interval $[a,b]$ means that there exists a number k such that, if D is a finite collection of nonoverlapping intervals filling up $[a,b]$, then the sum of the absolute values of the g-lengths of the intervals of D does not exceed k. If g is of bounded variation on $[a,b]$, the least such number k is denoted by $V_a^b \, g$ and called the total variation of g on $[a,b]$.

If the simple graph g has X-projection including $[a,b]$, then the following two statements are equivalent:

(i) g has length on $[a,b]$,

and

(ii) g is of bounded variation on $[a,b]$.

Theorem. If the simple graph f has X-projection $[a,b]$ and property (S) at each of its points and the simple graph g is of bounded variation on $[a,b]$, then f is g-integrable on $[a,b]$.

Problem. If each of f and g is one of the simple graphs, I, A, T, S, C, K, B, L, E, $\boldsymbol{S}$, or $\mathscr{C}$, to evaluate $\int_a^b f \, dg$.

Exercise. Suppose g is the simple graph defined by

$$g(x) = \begin{cases} -1/2, & \text{if } x < 0, \\ 0, & \text{if } x = 0, \\ 1/2, & \text{if } x > 0. \end{cases}$$

If the X-projection of f includes $[-1,1]$ and f has property (S) at $(0, f(0))$, then $\int_{-1}^1 f \, dg = f(0)$.

Theorem. If the simple graph g is nondecreasing on $[a,b]$ and if f is bounded and g-integrable on $[a,b]$, then $|f|$ is g-integrable on $[a,b]$ and

$$\left| \int_a^b f \, dg \right| \le \int_a^b |f| \, dg.$$

Moreover, if h is bounded and g-integrable on $[a,b]$, then fh is g-integrable on $[a,b]$ and

$$\left\{\int_a^b fh\ dg\right\}^2 \le \left\{\int_a^b f^2\ dg\right\} \cdot \left\{\int_a^b h^2\ dg\right\}.$$

EXTENDED INTEGRALS

Theorem. If f is a simple graph such that, if $h|$ is a vertical line there is a point of f to the right of $h|$, then the following statements are equivalent:

(i) if c is a positive number, there exists a vertical line $h|$ such that, if P and Q are points of f to the right of $h|$, the ordinate of P differs from the ordinate of Q by less than c; and

(ii) there exists a number k such that, if α and β are horizontal lines with $\underline{k}$ between them, there is a vertical line $h|$ such that every point of f to the right of $h|$ is between α and β.

Example. If we add the point $(0,1)$ to the simple graph S/I, the resulting simple graph has X-projection the set of all numbers and has property (S) at each of its points. Suppose this has been done, and define the simple graph f by

$$f(x) = \int_0^x \frac{S}{I}.$$

Now, if x and y are numbers and $0 < x < y$, then

$$f(y) - f(x) = \int_x^y \frac{S}{I} = \int_x^y \frac{1}{I} \cdot \{-C\}' = \frac{C(x)}{x} - \frac{C(y)}{y} - \int_x^y \frac{C}{(I^2)}$$

so that

$$|f(y) - f(x)| \le \frac{2}{x} + \int_x^y \left(-\frac{1}{I}\right)' = \frac{3}{x} - \frac{1}{y} < \frac{3}{x}.$$

Consequently, if c is a positive number and P and Q are points of f to the right of the vertical line $\frac{3}{c}|$, then the ordinate of P differs from the ordinate of Q by less than c; *i.e.*, statement (i) of the theorem is true. Hence statement (ii) is true. The number k of that statement we denote by

$$\int_0^{+\infty} \frac{S}{I},$$

called an *extended* integral.

We have seen that statement (ii) holds for the simple graph **A**, with k the number $\frac{\pi}{2}$. Thus, another extended integral is

$$\int_0^{+\infty} \frac{1}{1 + I^2} = \frac{\pi}{2}.$$

Note. It is true that

$$\int_0^{+\infty} \frac{S}{I} = \frac{\pi}{2}.$$

If this is taken for granted, it may be shown that

$$\frac{1}{\pi} \int_0^{+\infty} \frac{S[xI]}{I} = \begin{cases} \dfrac{1}{2}, & \text{if } x > 0, \\ 0, & \text{if } x = 0, \\ -\dfrac{1}{2} & \text{if } x < 0. \end{cases}$$

Exercise. Investigate in an analogous way the integrals

(i) $\int_0^x \frac{1 - C}{(I^2)}$ and (ii) $\int_0^x E[-I^2]$.

Note. If the point $(0, \frac{1}{2})$ is added to $\frac{1 - C}{I^2}$ the resulting simple graph has X-projection the set of all numbers and property (S) at each of its points. We suppose this has been done in (i).

NUMBER SEQUENCES

The statement that s is a *number sequence* means that s is a simple graph whose X-projection is the set of all positive integers. If s is a number sequence, we may write s_n for $s(n)$, the ordinate of that point of s whose abscissa is the positive integer n. A number sequence s for which the equivalent statements (i) and (ii) of the last theorem are true is called a *convergent number sequence* and is said to *converge* to the *sequential limit* k, where k is the number in statement (ii).

Example. Suppose, for each positive integer n, e_n is one of the numbers 1 or -1 and

$$s_n = 1 + \frac{1}{2} e_1 + \left(\frac{1}{2}\right)^2 e_2 + \ldots + \left(\frac{1}{n}\right)^n e_n.$$

Then s is a convergent number sequence.

Suppose, for each positive integer n, a_n is a number, $s_n = a_1 + a_2 + \ldots + a_n$ and $t_n = |a_1| + |a_2| + \ldots + |a_n|$. The following statements are true:

(i) the number sequence t is a convergent number sequence only in case there is a number h such that $t_n \leq h$, $n = 1, 2, 3, \ldots$; and

(ii) if t is convergent, then s is convergent.

If $s_n = 1 - \dfrac{1}{2} + \dfrac{1}{3} - \ldots + (-1)^{n-1} \cdot \dfrac{1}{n}$, $n = 1, 2, 3 \ldots$ and $t_n = 1 + \dfrac{1}{2} + \dfrac{1}{3} + \ldots + \dfrac{1}{n}$, then s is convergent but t is not convergent.

Problem. Suppose, for each positive integer n, x_n is a number, $x_n > x_{n+1} > 0$, the number sequence x has the sequential limit 0, and $s_n = x_n \mathrm{L}(x_n)$. Show that s is a convergent number sequence with the sequential limit 0. Hence show that, if the point $(0,0)$ is added to the simple graph IL, the resulting simple graph has property (S) at $(0,0)$.

TWO QUESTIONS

(i) Investigate simple graphs having property (Q) defined as follows. The statement that the simple graph f has property (Q) at the point P means that P is a point of f and there exists a point P_R whose abscissa is the abscissa of P and a point P_L whose abscissa is the abscissa of P such that, if A_R and B_R are horizontal lines with P_R between them and A_L and B_L are horizontal lines with P_L between them, then there exist vertical lines H and K with P between them such that every point of f between H and K to the right of P is between A_R and B_R and every point of f between H and K to the left of P is between A_L and B_L.

(ii) Investigate integrability defined as follows. The statement that f is *mean-integrable* with respect to g on $[a,b]$ means that each of f and g is a simple graph whose X-projection includes the interval $[a,b]$ and there exists a number J such that, if c is a positive number, there is a finite collection D of nonoverlapping intervals filling up $[a,b]$ such that, if D' is a finite collection of nonoverlapping intervals filling up $[a,b]$, with each end of each interval of D an end of some interval of D', and the g-length of each interval of D' is multiplied by one-half the sum of the ordinates of the points of f whose abscissas are the ends of that interval, then the sum of all the products so formed differs from J by less than c.

Simple Surfaces

The statement that f is a *simple surface* means that f is a collection, each element of which is an ordered pair (P,z), whose first or left-most member P is a point and whose second or right-most member z is a number, such that no two ordered pairs in f have the same first member. The second member of that ordered pair in f whose first member is P is denoted by $f(P)$ (read *f of* P) or, if $P = (x, y)$, by $f(x,y)$ (read *f of x and y*).

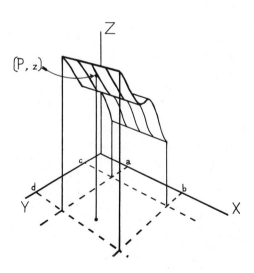

Problem. Generalize to simple surfaces some of the ideas concerning simple graphs such as slope, property (S), length, and integral.

To picture a simple surface, we regard the plane of points, the XY-plane, as horizontal and represent the ordered pair (P, z) of f as a dot on the vertical line containing P at a distance z above the XY-plane if $z > 0$, at P if $z = 0$, and below the XY-plane a distance $|z|$ if $z < 0$ (see figure).

The XY-projection of f is the point set to which P belongs only if P is the first member of an ordered pair in f. In the figure, the XY-projection of f is the rectangular interval $[ab; cd]$.

GRADIENT

In order to generalize to simple surfaces the notion of slope of a simple graph, we first reformulate our definition of slope of a simple graph. To avoid the use of pairs of vertical lines, we use the *segment*, which is the set of all numbers *between* two given numbers; *i.e.*, a segment is an interval minus its ends.

Definition. The statement that the simple graph f has slope at the point $(x, f(x))$ of f means that there exists *only one* number m such that, if c is a positive number, there exists a segment s containing x such that, if y is in s and in the X-projection of f, then

$$f(y) - f(x) = (y - x) \cdot m + |y - x| \cdot \begin{bmatrix} \text{a number between} \\ -c \text{ and } c \end{bmatrix} .$$

This is equivalent to the earlier definition. The requirement that there should be only one number m satisfying the condition implies that each two vertical lines with $(x, f(x))$ between them have between them a point of f distinct from $(x, f(x))$. The use of $|y - x|$ instead of $(y - x)$ in the second term of the right-hand member of the above equation amounts only to a possible change in sign in the number represented by the square-bracketed expression.

A *rectangular segment* is a rectangular interval minus its edges.

Definition. The statement that the simple surface f has *gradient* at the ordered pair $((x, y), f(x, y))$ of f means that there exists only one ordered number pair $\{p, q\}$ such that, if c is a positive number, there exists a rectangular segment s containing (x, y) such that, if (u, v) is in s and in the XY-projection of f, then

$$f(u, v) - f(x, y) = (u - x) \cdot p + (v - y) \cdot q + |(u, v) - (x, y)| \cdot \begin{bmatrix} \text{a number be-} \\ \text{tween } -c \text{ and } c \end{bmatrix} .$$

If f has gradient at $((x,y), f(x,y))$, the ordered number pair $\{p,q\}$ of this definition is called the *gradient* of f at $((x,y), f(x,y))$.

The statement that the simple graph f is *continuous* at the point P means that f has property (S) at P. We have used the term *property* (S) instead of *continuous* because the word continuous is somewhat misleading as applied to the concept in question. Continuous, as applied to a simple graph, does not mean that the graph is "all in one piece" as the word might imply when used in connection with physical things.

The statement that the simple surface f is continuous at $(P,f(P))$ means that $(P,f(P))$ is an ordered pair in f and, if c is a positive number, there exists a rectangular segment s containing P such that, if Q is a point of s belonging to the XY-projection of f, then $f(P)$ differs from $f(Q)$ by less than c.

Theorem. If the simple surface f has gradient at $(P,f(P))$, then f is continuous at $(P, f(P))$.

There are certain interesting simple graphs connected with a simple surface f. Suppose h is a number which is the ordinate of a point in the XY-projection of f, and denote by $f[I,h]$ the simple graph to which the point (x,y) belongs only if (x,h) is in the XY-projection of f and y is $f(x,h)$ (see figure). Likewise, if k is a number which is the abscissa of a point in the XY-projection of f, then $f[k,I]$ denotes the simple graph to which the point (x,y) belongs only if (k,x) is in the XY-projection of f and y is $f(k,x)$.

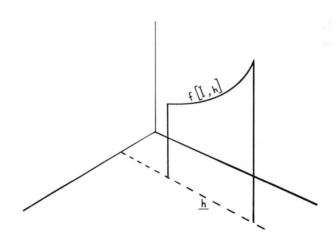

If there is a number h such that the simple graph $f[\mathrm{I},h]$ has slope at one of its points, then f_1', called the 1-derivative of f, is the simple surface to which the ordered pair $((x,y),z)$ belongs only if $f[\mathrm{I},y]$ has slope at $(x,f[\mathrm{I},y](x))$ and $z = \mathrm{D}_x f[\mathrm{I},y]$.

Example. If $f(x,y) = x^2 + 2xy + y^2$, then $f_1'(x,y) = \mathrm{D}_x(\mathrm{I}^2 + 2\mathrm{I}y + y^2)$ $= 2x + 2y$.

Similarly, f_2', the 2-*derivative* of f, is the simple surface to which $((x,y),z)$ belongs only if $f[x,\mathrm{I}]$ has slope at $(y,f[x,\mathrm{I}](y))$ and $z = \mathrm{D}_y f[x,\mathrm{I}]$.

If f is the simple surface of the above example, then $f_2'(x,y) = \mathrm{D}_{y|}(x^2 + 2x\mathrm{I} + \mathrm{I}^2) = 2x + 2y$.

For all appropriate points (x,y):

$$f_1'(x,y) = \mathrm{D}_x f[\mathrm{I},y] \quad \text{and} \quad f_2'(x,y) = \mathrm{D}_y f[x,\mathrm{I}].$$

Exercise. Compute $f_1'(x,y)$ and $f_2'(x,y)$ in each of the following cases:

(i) $\qquad\qquad\qquad f(x,y) = \mathrm{S}(x) + \mathrm{C}(y),$

(ii) $\qquad\qquad\qquad f(x,y) = \mathrm{L}(x^2 + 4y^2),$

(iii) $\qquad\qquad\qquad f(x,y) = x^3 - 5x^2 y + 2xy^2.$

The simple surfaces f_1' and f_2' are called the *first partial derivatives* of the simple surface f. There are four *second partial derivatives*: $(f_1')_1'$, $(f_1')_2'$, $(f_2')_1'$, and $(f_2')_2'$ denoted by f_{11}'', f_{12}'', f_{21}'', and f_{22}'', respectively, and called the 11-*derivative*, the 12-*derivative*, the 21-*derivative*, and the 22-*derivative*, of f.

Theorem. Suppose the simple surface f has XY-projection the rectangular interval $[ab;cd]$ and has gradient $\{p,q\}$ at $((x,y),f(x,y))$. Then

$$p = f_1'(x,y) \quad \text{and} \quad q = f_2'(x,y).$$

Theorem. If f, f_1', and f_2' have XY-projections including the rectangular segment s containing the point (x,y), f_1' is continuous at $((x,y),f_1'(x,y))$, and f_2' is continuous at $((x,y),f_2'(x,y))$, then f has gradient at $((x,y),f(x,y))$.

COMBINATIONS OF SIMPLE SURFACES

Suppose each of f and g is a simple surface and there is a point common to the XY-projection of f and the XY-projection of g. The *sum* $f + g$ is defined by

$$(f + g)(P) = f(P) + g(P)$$

and the *product* $f \cdot g$ by

$$(f \cdot g)(P) = f(P) \cdot g(P) ,$$

for every point P common to the XY-projection of f and the XY-projection of g; and, if P is a point such that $g(P) \neq 0$, the *reciprocal* $(1/g)$ is defined by

$$\frac{1}{g}(P) = \frac{1}{g(P)}$$

and the *quotient* (f/g) by $f \cdot (1/g)$.

Problem. Investigate the question of continuity of the sum, product, and quotient of continuous f and g.

Theorem. Suppose each of f and g is a simple surface and the rectangular segment s containing the point P is included in the common part of the XY-projections of f and g. If f has gradient at $(P, f(P))$ and g has gradient at $(P, g(P))$, then

(i) $f + g$ has gradient $\{f_1'(P) + g_1'(P), f_2'(P) + g_2'(P)\}$ at $(P, (f+g)(P))$,

(ii) $f \cdot g$ has gradient $\{f(P)g_1'(P) + g(P)f_1'(P), f(P)g_2'(P) + g(P)f_2'(P)\}$ at $(P, (f \cdot g)(P))$ and

(iii) if $g(P) \neq 0$, (f/g) has gradient

$$\left\{ \frac{g(P)f_1'(P) - f(P)g_1'(P)}{g^2(P)} , \frac{g(P)f_2'(P) - f(P)g_2'(P)}{g^2(P)} \right\} \quad \text{at} \quad (P, \frac{f}{g}(P)).$$

Suppose each of f, g, and h is a simple surface and there is a point P common to the XY-projection of g and the XY-projection of h and the point $(g(P), h(P))$ belongs to the XY-projection of f. The *bracket product* $f[g,h]$ (read f *of* g *and* h) is defined for all such P by

$$f[g,h](P) = f(g(P), h(P)).$$

Under suitable conditions, which we leave unstated,

$$(f[g,h])_1' = f_1'[g,h]g_1' + f_2'[g,h]h_1'$$

and

$$(f[g,h])_2' = f_1'[g,h]g_2' + f_2'[g,h]h_2'.$$

MORE SIMPLE GRAPHS DETERMINED BY A SIMPLE SURFACE

Suppose each of g and h is a simple graph with X-projection the interval $[a,b]$ such that, if t is in $[a,b]$, $(g(t), h(t))$ is a point in the XY-projection of the simple surface f. Then, another kind of bracket product is the simple graph $f[g,h]$ with X-projection $[a,b]$ defined, for each t in $[a,b]$, by

$$f[g,h](t) = f(g(t), h(t)).$$

Theorem. If f has XY-projection the rectangular segment s and has gradient at each of its ordered pairs and each of g' and h' has X-projection including the number t of $[a,b]$, then

$$D_t f[g,h] = f_1'[g,h](t) \cdot g'(t) + f_2'[g,h](t) \cdot h'(t).$$

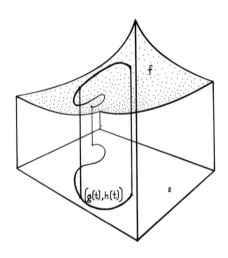

Example. If $g = x + u\mathrm{I}$ and $h = y + v\mathrm{I}$, where each of x, y, u, and v is a suitable number, then

$$D_t f[g,h] = D_t f[x + u\mathrm{I}, y + v\mathrm{I}] = f_1'(x + ut, y + vt) \cdot u + f_2'(x + ut, y + vt) \cdot v.$$

Theorem. Suppose f is a simple surface which has gradient at each of its ordered pairs and XY-projection the rectangular segment s and g is a simple graph whose X-projection is the interval $[a,b]$, continuous at each of its points, and, for each t in $[a,b]$, the point

$(t, g(t))$ is in s and $f(t, g(t)) = 0$. Then, for each number t in $[a,b]$ for which $f_2'(t, g(t)) \neq 0$:

$$g'(t) = -\frac{f_1'(t, g(t))}{f_2'(t, g(t))} \ .$$

Example. If $f(x,y) = x^2 + y^2 - 1$ and g is one of the simple graphs $Q[1 - I^2]$ or $-Q[1 - I^2]$, then $f(t, g(t)) = 0$ for every number t in the interval $[-1,1]$. Also, $f_1'(x,y) = 2x$ and $f_2'(x,y) = 2y$. Consequently, if $-1 < t < 1$:

$$g'(t) = -\frac{t}{g(t)} \ ;$$

i.e., $D_t \, Q[1 - I^2] = -\dfrac{t}{Q(1 - t^2)} \ .$

Exercise. If, for every point (x,y) such that $y > 0$, $f(x,y) = x - L(y)$, then $f(x, E(x)) = 0$ for every number x. Apply the preceding theorem to show that $E' = E$. Investigate, in the same way, $x - A(y)$ and $x - S(y)$.

g - AREA OF A RECTANGULAR INTERVAL

The area of the rectangular interval $[ab; cd]$ is the number $(b - a)(d - c)$ or $bd - bc - ad + ac$ so that, if J is the simple surface such that, if (x,y) is a point, $J(x,y) = xy$, then the area of $[ab; cd]$ is $J(b,d) - J(b,c) - J(a,d) + J(a,c)$. This observation suggests the following generalization of the notion of area.

Definition. The statement that $g\big|_a^b\big|_c^d$ is the g-area of the rectangular interval $[ab; cd]$ means that g is a simple surface whose

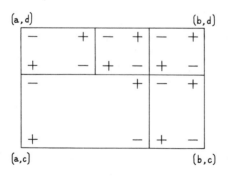

XY-projection includes $[ab;cd]$ and

$$g\left|\begin{matrix} b \\ a \end{matrix}\right|\begin{matrix} d \\ c \end{matrix} = g(b,d) - g(b,c) - g(a,d) + g(a,c).$$

We note that

$$g\left|\begin{matrix} b \\ a \end{matrix}\right|\begin{matrix} d \\ c \end{matrix} = \{g[b,\mathrm{I}] - g[a,\mathrm{I}]\}\left|\begin{matrix} d \\ c \end{matrix}\right. = \{g(b,d) - g(a,d)\} - \{g(b,c) - g(a,c)\} = g\left|\begin{matrix} d \\ c \end{matrix}\right|\begin{matrix} b \\ a \end{matrix}.$$

This generalization has the fundamental property of ordinary area that, if D is a finite collection of rectangular intervals which are nonoverlapping and fill up $[ab;cd]$, then the sum of the g-areas of the rectangular intervals of D is $g\left|\begin{matrix} b \\ a \end{matrix}\right|\begin{matrix} d \\ c \end{matrix}$.

Theorem. Suppose g is a simple surface whose XY-projection includes $[ab;cd]$ such that the XY-projection of the 12-derivative g_{12}'' (or of the 21-derivative g_{21}'') includes $[ab;cd]$. There exists a point (u,v) interior to $[ab;cd]$ (*i.e.*, $a < u < b$, $c < v < d$) such that

$$g\left|\begin{matrix} b \\ a \end{matrix}\right|\begin{matrix} d \\ c \end{matrix} = g''(u,v) \cdot (b-a)(d-c),$$

where g'' denotes g_{12}'' or g_{21}'' according to the case.

Corollary. Suppose each of g, g_{12}'', and g_{21}'' has XY-projection $[ab;cd]$ and each of g_{12}'' and g_{21}'' is continuous at each of its ordered pairs. Then $g_{12}'' = g_{21}''$.

If g is the simple surface defined by

$$g(x,y) = \begin{cases} 0, & \text{if } (x,y) = (0,0), \\ \dfrac{xy(x^2 - y^2)}{x^2 + y^2}, & \text{if } (x,y) \neq (0,0), \end{cases}$$

then $g_{12}''(0,0) \neq g_{21}''(0,0)$.

MAXIMA AND MINIMA

Suppose f is a simple surface with XY-projection the rectangular segment s such that each of the second partial derivatives of f has XY-projection s and is continuous at each of its ordered pairs. Then $f_{12}'' = f_{21}''$. If (x,y) and $(x+h, y+k)$ are points of s and, for each number t in $[0,1]$, $F(t) = f(x+ht, y+kt)$, then

$$F(1) - F(0) = \int_0^1 F' = \int_0^1 F' \cdot (\mathrm{I} - 1)' = F'(0) - \int_0^1 F'' \cdot \left[\frac{(\mathrm{I} - 1)^2}{2}\right]'$$

so that there exists a number θ in the interval $[0,1]$ such that

$$f(x + h, y + k) - f(x,y) = f'_1(x,y) \cdot h + f'_2(x,y) \cdot k$$

$$+ \tfrac{1}{2}\{f''_{11}(x + \theta h, y + \theta k)h^2 + 2f''_{12}(x + \theta h, y + \theta k)hk + f''_{22}(x + \theta h, y + \theta k)k^2\}.$$

Corollary. If P is a point of s such that $f'_1(P) = 0$ and $f'_2(P) = 0$ and $f''_{11}(P)f''_{22}(P) - \{f''_{12}(P)\}^2 > 0$, then

(i) if $f''_{11}(P) > 0$, there exists a rectangular segment δ containing P such that, if Q is a point of δ distinct from P, $f(Q) > f(P)$ and

(ii) if $f''_{11}(P) < 0$, there exists a rectangular segment δ containing P such that, if Q is a point of δ distinct from P, $f(Q) < f(P)$.

Exercise. Let f be the simple surface defined, for each point (x,y) such that $x + y \neq 0$, by

$$f(x,y) = \frac{xy(1 - xy)}{x + y} .$$

Find a point P such that, for some rectangular segment δ containing P, $f(Q) < F(P)$ for every point Q in δ which is distinct from P.

INTEGRAL OF A SIMPLE SURFACE WITH RESPECT TO A SIMPLE SURFACE

The statement that the simple surface g *is nondecreasing* on $[ab; cd]$ means that the g-area of each rectangular interval included in $[ab; cd]$ is nonnegative. The statement that the simple surface f *is bounded* on $[ab; cd]$ means that there exists a number k such that, if P is in $[ab; cd]$, $|f(P)| \leq k$.

If the simple surface f is bounded and g nondecreasing on $[ab; cd]$, inner sum, outer sum, inner integral, and outer integral are defined as in the case of simple graphs. The statement that $_iS$ is an *inner sum* for f with respect to g on $[ab; cd]$ means that there exists a finite collection D of nonoverlapping rectangular intervals filling up $[ab; cd]$ such that, if the g-area of each rectangular interval in D is multiplied by the largest number which does not exceed $f(P)$ for any point P in that rectangular interval, then the sum of all the products so formed is $_iS$. For outer sum $_oS$, replace "largest number which does not exceed $f(P)$" by "smallest number which $f(P)$ does not exceed," in this statement. If $V \leq f(P) \leq U$ for every point P in $[ab; cd]$, then

$$V \cdot g\Big|_a^b\Big|_c^d \leq {}_iS \leq {}_oS \leq U \cdot g\Big|_a^b\Big|_c^d \,;$$

the inner integral of f with respect to g on $[ab; cd]$, denoted by

$$_i\int_a^b \int_c^d f\,dg,$$

is the least number which no inner sum for f with respect to g on $[ab;cd]$ exceeds; and the outer integral of f with respect to g on $[ab;cd]$, denoted by

$$_0\int_a^b \int_c^d f\,dg,$$

is the largest number which exceeds no outer sum for f with respect to g on $[ab;cd]$. There is the inequality,

$$V \cdot g\Big|_a^b \Big|_c^d \leq\; _iS \leq\; _i\int_a^b \int_c^d f\,dg \leq\; _0\int_a^b \int_c^d f\,dg \leq\; _0S \leq U \cdot g\Big|_a^b \Big|_c^d .$$

Theorem. If f is bounded and g nondecreasing on $[ab;cd]$, then each two of the following four statements are equivalent:

(i) $_i\int_a^b \int_c^d f\,dg = _0\int_a^b \int_c^d f\,dg,$

(ii) if c is a positive number there exists an inner sum $_iS$ for f with respect to g on $[ab;cd]$ and an outer sum $_0S$ for f with respect to g on $[ab;cd]$ such that $_0S$ and $_iS$ differ by less than c,

(iii) if each of c and d is a positive number, there exists a finite collection D of nonoverlapping intervals filling up $[ab;cd]$ such that, if there is a rectangular interval in D containing two points P and Q for which $f(P)$ differs from $f(Q)$ by more than c, then the sum of the g-areas of all such rectangular intervals in D is less than d,

(iv) there exists a number w such that, if c is a positive number, there exists a finite collection D of nonoverlapping rectangular intervals filling up $[ab;cd]$ such that, if D$'$ is a finite collection of nonoverlapping rectangular intervals filling up $[ab;cd]$, with each point of each edge of a rectangular interval of D a point of an edge of some rectangular interval of D$'$, and, if the g-area of each rectangular interval in D$'$ is multiplied by $f(P)$, where P is any point in that rectangular interval, then the sum of all the products so formed differs from w by less than c.

Definition. If each of f and g is a simple surface whose XY-projection includes the rectangular interval $[ab;cd]$, the statement that f is g-integrable on $[ab;cd]$ means that there exists a number w for which statement (iv) of the preceding Theorem is true. If f is g-integrable on $[ab;cd]$, this number w is called the integral of f with respect to g on $[ab;cd]$ and is denoted by

$$\int_a^b \int_c^d f \, dg.$$

The statement that $\underline{k}$ is a horizontal plane, means that k is a number and $\underline{k}$ the simple surface f such that, for every point P, the second member of the ordered pair in f whose first member is P is the number k.

If the XY-projection of g includes $[ab; cd]$ and k is a number,

$$\int_a^b \int_c^d \underline{k} \, dg = k \cdot g \Big|_a^b \Big|_c^d .$$

If f is g-integrable and fg'', where g'' is g_{12}'' or g_{21}'', is J-integrable on $[ab; cd]$, then

$$\int_a^b \int_c^d f \, dg = \int_a^b \int_c^d fg'' \, dJ.$$

($J(x,y) = xy$, for every point (x,y)).

If, in particular, g'' is J-integrable on $[ab; cd]$ ($J(x,y) = xy$), then

$$\int_a^b \int_c^d g'' \, dJ = g \Big|_a^b \Big|_c^d .$$

The statement that the simple surface g is of bounded variation on $[ab; cd]$ means the XY-projection of g includes $[ab; cd]$ and there exists a number k such that, if D is a finite collection of nonoverlapping rectangular intervals filling up $[ab; cd]$, then the sum of the absolute values of the g-areas of the rectangular intervals of D does not exceed k.

Theorem. If the simple surface f has XY-projection the rectangular interval $[ab; cd]$ and is continuous at each of its ordered pairs and if the simple surface g is of bounded variation on $[ab; cd]$, then f is g-integrable on $[ab; cd]$.

Note. A sufficient condition for f to be "continuous on $[ab; cd]$" is for f_1' and f_2' to be bounded on $[ab; cd]$.

Theorem. Suppose the simple surface f has XY-projection the rectangular interval $[ab; cd]$ and, if c is a positive number, there exists a finite collection D of nonoverlapping rectangular intervals filling up $[ab; cd]$ such that, if there is a rectangular interval in D containing a point P such that f is not continuous at $(P, f(P))$, then the sum of the areas of all such rectangular intervals in D is less than c. Suppose, moreover, that f is bounded on $[ab; cd]$. Then f is J-integrable on $[ab; cd]$.

Example.   If $g = J^2/4$, then $g'' = J$ and, consequently,

$$\int_a^b \int_c^d J\, dJ = \frac{J^2}{4} \left|\begin{array}{c} b \\ a \end{array}\right. \left|\begin{array}{c} d \\ c \end{array}\right. = \frac{1}{4} \{ (ac)^2 - (bc)^2 + (bd)^2 - (ad)^2 \} .$$

Exercise.   Evaluate the integral

$$\int_a^b \int_c^d J^n\, dJ,$$

where n is an integer.

The statement that W is a *point in 3-space* means that W is an ordered number triple (x,y,z). Suppose f is a simple surface whose XY-projection includes the point set M. The region $[f;M]$ in 3-space determined by f and M is the point set in 3-space to which (x,y,z) belongs only if (x,y) is a point of M and z is 0, z is $f(x,y)$, or z is a number between 0 and $f(x,y)$.

If the XY-projection of f includes $[ab;cd]$ and $f(P) \geq 0$ for every point P in $[ab;cd]$, then the *volume* of the region $[f;[ab;cd]]$ in 3-space is the integral

$$\int_a^b \int_c^d f\, dJ.$$

Exercise.   Find the volume of each of the regions in 3-space indicated:

(i) $[f;[01;01]]$, where $f(x,y) = 12xy^2 + 8y$,

(ii) $[f;[12;12]]$, where $f(x,y) = \dfrac{1}{(x + y)^2}$,

(iii) $[f;[01;01]]$, where $f(x,y) = x \cdot \mathrm{E}(\ x^2)$,

(iv) $[f;[0b;0d]]$, where $b > 0,\ d > 0$ and $f(x,y) = \mathrm{Q}(b^2 - x^2)$

and

(v) $[f;[01;01]]$, where $f(x,y) = 1 - x$.

Problem.   Suppose r is a positive number and, for each point (x,y) in $[0r;0r]$,

$$f(x,y) = \begin{cases} \mathrm{Q}(r^2 - x^2 - y^2), & \text{if } x^2 + y^2 \leq r^2, \\ 0, & \text{if } x^2 + y^2 > r^2. \end{cases}$$

Sketch f and try to compute the volume of $[f;[0r;0r]]$.

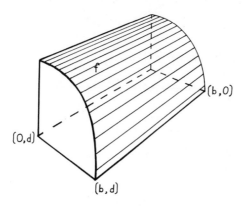

ITERATED INTEGRALS

Theorem. Suppose the simple surface f has XY-projection $[ab;cd]$ and is continuous at each of its ordered pairs.

(i) If h is the simple graph with X-projection $[a,b]$ such that, for each number x in $[a,b]$,

$$h(x) = \int_c^d f[x,I],$$

then h is continuous at each of its points.

(ii) Suppose, for each point (s,t) in $[ab;cd]$,

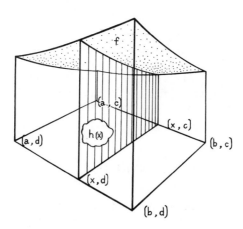

103

$$h(s,t) = \int_0^t f[s,\mathrm{I}]$$

and, for each point (x,y) in $[ab;cd]$,

$$g(x,y) = \int_a^x h[\mathrm{I},y].$$

Then $f = g_{12}''$.

Corollary. $\displaystyle\int_a^b \int_c^d f \, d\mathrm{J} = \int_a^b \int_c^d g_{12}'' \, d\mathrm{J} = g\Big|_a^b\Big|_c^d$,

or

$$\int_a^b \int_c^d f \, d\mathrm{J} = \int_a^b h[\mathrm{I},d],$$

where

$$h(x,d) = \int_c^d f[x,\mathrm{I}].$$

That is, with x "fixed," $h(x,d)$ is the integral from c to d of $f[x,\mathrm{I}]$ and $\displaystyle\int_a^b \int_c^d f \, d\mathrm{J}$ is the integral from a to b of $h[\mathrm{I},d]$.

Note. It is convenient to write this result in the form,

$$\int_a^b \int_c^d f \, d\mathrm{J} = \int_a^b \left\{ \int_c^d f(x,y)\,dy \right\} dx .$$

Of course, there is also the formula,

$$\int_a^b \int_c^d f \, d\mathrm{J} = \int_c^d \left\{ \int_a^b f(x,y)\,dx \right\} dy .$$

These formulas are to be interpreted as in the above corollary. The integrals in the right-hand members are called *iterated integrals*. In the preceding figure, $h(x,d)$, or $h(x)$, is the area of a "plane cross-section" of the region $[f;[ab;cd]]$ in 3-space. The volume is then $\int_a^b h$.

CASE WHERE f IS NOT CONTINUOUS

Theorem

(i) If f is J-integrable on $[ab;cd]$, then f is bounded on $[ab;cd]$.

(ii) If f is J-integrable on $[ab;cd]$, for each number x in $[a,b]$,

$g(x) = {}_i\!\int_c^d f[x,\mathrm{I}]$ and, for each number y in $[c,d]$, $h(y) = {}_i\!\int_a^b f[\mathrm{I},y]$, then

$$\int_a^b \int_c^d f\, d\mathrm{J} = \int_a^b g = \int_c^d h.$$

(iii) If, in particular, $f[x,\mathrm{I}]$ is integrable on $[c,d]$ for every x in $[a,b]$, then

$$\int_a^b \int_c^d f\, d\mathrm{J} = \int_a^b \left\{ \int_c^d f(x,y)\, dy \right\} dx;$$

and, if $f[\mathrm{I},y]$ is integrable on $[a,b]$ for every y in $[c,d]$, then

$$\int_a^b \int_c^d f\, d\mathrm{J} = \int_c^d \left\{ \int_a^b f(x,y)\, dx \right\} dy.$$

Thus, if f is J-integrable on $[ab; cd]$ and both the iterated integrals exist,

$$\int_a^b \int_c^d f\, d\mathrm{J} = \int_a^b \left\{ \int_c^d f(x,y)\, dy \right\} dx = \int_c^d \left\{ \int_a^b f(x,y)\, dx \right\} dy.$$

Note. The iterated integrals may be written without the braces as

$$\int_a^b \int_c^d f(x,y)\, dy\, dx \quad \text{and} \quad \int_c^d \int_a^b f(x,y)\, dx\, dy,$$

or as

$$\int_a^b dx \int_c^d f(x,y)\, dy \quad \text{and} \quad \int_c^d dy \int_a^b f(x,y)\, dx.$$

INTEGRAL OVER A POINT SET

Suppose M is a subset of the rectangular interval $[ab; cd]$. The statement that *f is g-integrable on* M means that each of f and g is a simple surface, the XY-projection of f includes M, that of g includes $[ab; cd]$ and, if F is the simple surface whose XY-projection is $[ab; cd]$ defined by:

$$F(\mathrm{P}) = \begin{cases} f(\mathrm{P}), & \text{if } \mathrm{P} \text{ is in M}, \\ 0, & \text{if } \mathrm{P} \text{ is not in M}, \end{cases}$$

then F is g-integrable on $[ab; cd]$. In this case, the integral on M of f with respect to g is defined as the integral on $[ab; cd]$ of F with respect to g:

$$\iint\limits_{M} f\, dg = \int_a^b \int_c^d \mathbf{F}\, dg.$$

Theorem. Suppose each of u and v is a simple graph with X-projection $[a,b]$ and continuous at each of its points and, for each number x in $[a,b]$, $u(x) \leq v(x)$. Suppose M is the point set to which (x,y) belongs only if x is in $[a,b]$ and y is $u(x)$ or y is $v(x)$, or y is a number between $u(x)$ and $v(x)$. If f is a simple surface whose XY-projection is M and which is continuous at each of its ordered pairs, then f is J-integrable on M and

$$\iint\limits_{M} f\, d\mathbf{J} = \int_a^b g,$$

where, for each number x in $[a,b]$,

$$g(x) = \int_{u(x)}^{v(x)} f[x,\mathbf{I}].$$

This statement may be abbreviated as:

$$\iint\limits_{M} f\, d\mathbf{J} = \int_a^b \left\{ \int_{u(x)}^{v(x)} f(x,y)\, dy \right\} dx.$$

Exercise

(i) Suppose M is the point set to which (x,y) belongs only if $x^2 + y^2 \leq 1$ and $f(x,y) = x^2 + y^2 + 1$. Evaluate the integral $\iint\limits_{M} f\, d\mathbf{J}$.

(ii) Suppose a is a positive number. Find the volume of the region in 3-space to which (x,y,z) belongs only if $x^2 + z^2 \leq a^2$, $x^2 + y^2 \leq a^2$, $x \geq 0$, $y \geq 0$, $z \geq 0$.

(iii) Suppose each of a, b, and c is a positive number. Find the volume of the region in 3-space to which (x,y,z) belongs only if

$(x/a)^2 + (y/b)^2 + (z/c)^2 \leq 1$, $x \geq 0$ and $z \geq 0$. (Ans. $(\pi abc/6)$).

AREA OF A SIMPLE SURFACE

Addition, multiplication by numbers, and inner product are defined among points in 3-space as follows. If $P = (x,y,z)$, $Q = (u,v,w)$, and k is a number: $P + Q = (x+u, y+v, z+w)$, $k \cdot P = (kx,ky,kz)$ and $((P,Q)) = xu + yv + zw$. We identify the point (x,y) ("in 2-space")

with the point $(x,y,0)$ in 3-space. The distance from P to Q, denoted by $|P - Q|$, is the number $((P - Q, P - Q))^{1/2}$.

Definition. Suppose f is a simple surface with gradient $\{p,q\}$ at $(R, f(R))$. The statement that M is the *tangent plane to* f *at* $(R, f(R))$ means that M is the simple surface such that, if P is the point (x,y) and $R = (a,b)$, then

$$M(P) = p \cdot (x - a) + q \cdot (y - b) + f(R).$$

Note that $M(R) = f(R)$, $M_1'(R) = p$, and $M_2'(R) = q$. If, for instance, R is contained in a rectangular segment included in the XY-projection of f, then $M_1'(R) = f_1'(R)$ and $M_2'(R) = f_2'(R)$.

Definition. The statement that T is a transformation from the set A to the set B means that T is a collection of ordered pairs (a,b) such that a belongs to A, b to B, each element of A is the first member of an ordered pair in T, each element of B is the second member of an ordered pair in T, and no two ordered pairs in T have the same first member. If (a,b) is in T, then b is denoted by $T(a)$ or by Ta.

Examples. A simple graph is a transformation from a number set to a number set; a simple surface is a transformation from a point set to a number set.

The statement that the transformation T from the set A to the set B is *reversible* means that no two ordered pairs in T have the same second member. That is, the collection U of ordered pairs to which (b,a) belongs only if (a,b) belongs to T is a transformation from the set B to the set A; U is called the *inverse* of the transformation T. For example, the simple graph L is a transformation from the set of all positive numbers to the set of all numbers; and L is reversible, the inverse being the simple graph E which is a transformation from the set of all numbers to the set of all positive numbers.

Problem. Suppose f is a simple surface whose XY-projection includes the rectangular interval $[a, a + h; b, b + k]$, where h is a positive number and k a positive number, having gradient $\{p,q\}$ at $((a,b), f(a,b))$. Suppose M is the tangent plane to f at $((a,b), f(a,b))$:

$$M(x,y) = (x - a) \cdot p + (y - b) \cdot q + f(a,b),$$

and M_0 the subset of M whose XY-projection is $[a, a + h; b, b + k]$. What shall we mean by the *area* of M_0?

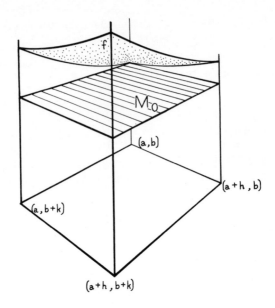

Let us identify the ordered pair $((x,y), M(x,y))$ of M with the point in 3-space $(x,y,M(x,y))$ and try to find a reversible transformation F from M_0 to a point set K such that "distances are preserved under the transformation"; *i.e.*, if $W_1 = (x,y, M(x,y))$ and $W_2 = (u,v, M(u,v))$, then

$$|W_1 - W_2| = |F(W_1) - F(W_2)| .$$

Such a transformation could be described as a "rigid motion" taking M_0 onto a region K in the XY-plane. If we can compute the area of K, we may assign to M_0 the same area.

For each point (x,y), we denote $(x - a, y - b)$ by (s,t), so that

$$x = a + s, \quad y = b + t.$$

Then,

$$M(x,y) = f(a,b) + p \cdot s + q \cdot t$$

and

$$(x,y, M(x,y)) = (a + s, b + t, f(a,b) + ps + qt)$$
$$= (a,b,f(a,b)) + s \cdot (1,0,p) + t \cdot (0,1,q).$$

Hence, if $W_0 = (a,b,f(a,b))$, $U_0 = (1,0,p)$, $V_0 = (0,1,q)$, then the point W in 3-space belongs to M only if there exists an ordered pair (s,t) such that

$$W = W_0 + s \cdot U_0 + t \cdot V_0 .$$

This defines a reversible transformation, consisting of the ordered pairs $(W,(s,t))$, from M to the set of all points.

If $W_1 = W_0 + s_1 \cdot U_0 + t_1 \cdot V_0$ and $W_2 = W_0 + s_2 \cdot U_0 + t_2 \cdot V_0$, the distance $|W_1 - W_2|$ is $(\!(W_1 - W_2, W_1 - W_2)\!)^{1/2}$ or,

$$|W_1 - W_2| = \{(s_1 - s_2)^2 |U_0|^2 + 2(s_1 - s_2)(t_1 - t_2)(\!(U_0,V_0)\!) + (t_1 - t_2)^2 |V_0|^2 \}^{1/2}.$$

If $|U_0| = 1$, $(\!(U_0,V_0)\!)) = 0$, and $|V_0| = 1$, this is the distance from (s_1,t_1) to (s_2,t_2).

To obtain a distance preserving transformation, we proceed as follows. Suppose

$$U = \frac{1}{|U_0|} \cdot U_0 ,$$

so that $|U| = 1$ and

$$U_0 = |U_0| \cdot U .$$

If c is a number, $(\!(U, c \cdot U + V_0)\!) = c + (\!(U,V_0)\!) = 0$ provided $c = -(\!(U,V_0)\!)$. Then, if

$$V = \frac{1}{|V_0 - (\!(U,V_0)\!) \cdot U|} \cdot \{V_0 - (\!(U,V_0)\!) \cdot U\},$$

we have $|V| = 1$ and $(\!(U,V)\!) = 0$. Also,

$$V_0 = |V_0 - (\!(U,V_0)\!) \cdot U| \cdot V + (\!(U,V_0)\!) \cdot U .$$

Hence, the point W in 3-space belongs to M only if there exists an ordered number pair (s,t) such that

$$W = W_0 + s \cdot |U_0| \cdot U + t \cdot \{|V_0 - (\!(U,V_0)\!) \cdot U| \cdot V + (\!(U,V_0)\!) \cdot U\}$$

$$= W_0 + u \cdot U + v \cdot V,$$

where

$$u = s|U_0| + t(\!(U,V_0)\!) \quad \text{and} \quad v = t|V_0 - (\!(U,V_0)\!) \cdot U| .$$

The relationship

$$W = W_0 + u \cdot U + v \cdot V$$

defines a reversible transformation F *from* M *to the set of all points* (u,v).

Since F is distance preserving, we have justified the name *plane* for M. There is a "rigid motion" which "carries" M onto the plane of all points (u,v).

The point (x,y) belongs to the XY-projection of M_0 only if (s,t) belongs to $[0,h;0,k]$ and only if (u,v) belongs to the "parallelogram disc" shown in the accompanying figure.

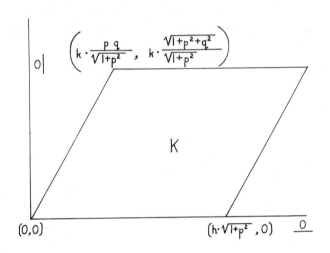

The area of this disc is

$$h \cdot k \cdot \sqrt{1 + p^2 + q^2}$$

We take this number to be the area of M_0.
We are now in a position to make the following definition.

Definition. If f is a simple surface whose XY-projection includes the point set G, and if $Q[1 + (f_1')^2 + (f_2')^2]$ is J-integrable on G, then *the area of* f *on* G *is*

$$\iint\limits_{G} Q[1 + (f_1')^2 + (f_2')^2] \, dJ.$$

Exercise. Suppose a is a positive number and M the point set to which (x,y) belongs only if $4x^2 + y^2 \le a^2$, $x \ge 0$, and $y \ge 0$. If

110

f is the simple surface whose XY-projection is M such that $f(x,y) = Q(a^2 - x^2 - y^2)$, show that the area of f is $\pi a^2/6$.

PATH INTEGRALS

We denote by $\{p(P), q(P)\}$ the gradient of the simple surface f at $(P, f(P))$ and define the number $\phi(P,Q)$ for every point Q in the XY-projection of f as follows: $\phi(P,P) = 0$ and, if $P = (x,y)$, $Q = (u,v)$, and $P \neq Q$, then

$$f(Q) - f(P) = (u - x)\cdot p(P) + (v - y)\cdot q(P) + |P - Q|\cdot\phi(P,Q) .$$

If c is a positive number, there exists a positive number d such that, if Q is in the XY-projection of f and $|P - Q| < d$, then

$$|\phi(P,Q)| < c .$$

If f has gradient at $(P, f(P))$ and at $(Q, f(Q))$, then

$$|\phi(P,Q)| \leq |P(Q) - p(P)| + |q(Q) - q(P)| + |\phi(Q,P)| .$$

The statement that the point set M is a *path* means that there exists an ordered pair x, y, each element of which is a simple graph with X-projection the interval $[0,1]$, continuous at each of its points, and having length, such that P belongs to M only if there exists a number t in $[0,1]$ for which $P = (x(t), y(t))$; the path M is denoted by $\{x,y\}_0^1$; the path is *closed* in case $x(0) = x(1)$ and $y(0) = y(1)$.

Theorem. Suppose f is a simple surface and M the path $\{x,y\}_0^1$ and

i. if P is in M, f has gradient $\{p(P), q(P)\}$ at $(P, f(P))$;

ii. if P is in M, p is continuous at $(P, p(P))$ and q at $(P, q(P))$; and

iii. each of x' and y' has X-projection $[0,1]$ and is continuous at each of its points.

Then,

$$\int_0^1 p[x,y]\, dx + \int_0^1 q[x,y]\, dy = \int_0^1 1\ df[x,y] = f[x,y]\ \Big|_0^1 .$$

Note. The same conclusion is true without the restrictive condition No. iii on x' and y'.

Theorem. Suppose each of p and q is a simple surface and, if P is a point in the rectangular segment s, p is continuous at $(P, p(P))$ and q at $(P, q(P))$ and, if $\{x,y\}_0^1$ is a closed path which is a subset of s,

$$\int_0^1 p[x,y]\,dx + \int_0^1 q[x,y]\,dy = 0 .$$

Then there exists a simple surface f with gradient $\{p(P), q(P)\}$ at $(P, f(P))$ for each point P of s.

VECTORS

A vector ("in the plane") is an ordered number pair $\{A,B\}$; A is the *horizontal component*, B the *vertical component* and $Q(A^2 + B^2)$ the *magnitude* of the vector $\{A,B\}$. The statement that θ is the *inclination* of the vector $\{A,B\}$ means that the magnitude r of $\{A,B\}$ is positive and θ is the number such that $0 \le \theta < 2\pi$, $A = r \cdot C(\theta)$, and $B = r \cdot S(\theta)$. If P is the point (x,y) and Q the point (u,v), the *vector from* P *to* Q is $\{u - x, v - y\}$.

Suppose f is a simple surface with gradient $\{p,q\}$ at $(P, f(P))$ and v is a vector with inclination θ. The *directional derivative* of f at $(P, f(P))$ *in the direction* v, denoted by

$$\frac{\partial f}{\partial v},$$

is the number $p \cdot C(\theta) + q \cdot S(\theta)$.

Theorem. Suppose f is a simple surface with gradient $\{p,q\}$ at $(P, f(P))$ and $p^2 + q^2 > 0$. Then, $\{p,q\}$ is a vector whose magnitude r is the maximum of the absolute values of the directional derivatives of f at $(P, f(P))$, and $\partial f/\partial v = r$ if v is one of the vectors $\{p,q\}$ or $\{-p,-q\}$, and $\partial f/\partial v = -r$ if v is the other one of these vectors. The absolute value of the directional derivative of f is less than r in any other direction.

ASSORTED THEOREMS AND PROBLEMS

Theorems
1. Suppose f is a simple surface with gradient at each of its ordered pairs and XY-projection the rectangular segment s. If P is a point of s such that $f(P) = 0$, $f_2'(P) \neq 0$, and f_2' is continuous at $(P, f_2'(P))$, then there exists a segment t containing the abscissa of P and a simple graph g whose X-projection is t such that g is continuous at each of its points and, if x is in the segment t, $f(x, g(x)) = 0$. Moreover, g has slope $-\dfrac{f_1'(x, g(x))}{f_2'(x, g(x))}$ at $(x, g(x))$ for

each x in t.

2. If the simple surface f has XY-projection $[ab;cd]$ and is continuous at each of its ordered pairs, if $f(P) \geq 0$ for every P in $[ab;cd]$, and if $\int_a^b \int_c^d f\,dJ = 0$, then $f(P) = 0$ for every P in $[ab;cd]$.

3. If each of f, g, and h is a simple surface, h is nondecreasing on $[ab;cd]$ and each of f and g bounded and h-integrable on $[ab;cd]$, then

$$\left(\int_a^b \int_c^d fg\,dh\right)^2 \leq \left(\int_a^b \int_c^d f^2\,dh\right)\left(\int_a^b \int_c^d g^2\,dh\right).$$

Problems

i. Denote the number $\int_0^{+\infty} \frac{S}{I}$ by k. To prove that $k = \frac{\pi}{2}$, assume that $|k - (\pi/2)| = \delta > 0$, and try to reach a contradiction. Let f be the simple surface defined by $f(x,y) = E(-xy)S(y)$. If $a > 0$, $b > 0$:

$$\int_0^a \int_0^b f\,dJ = \int_0^a \left\{\int_0^b E(-xy)S(y)\,dy\right\}dx = \int_0^b \left\{\int_0^a E(-xy)S(y)\,dx\right\}dy,$$

so that

$$\int_0^a \frac{1 - E[-bI]\{C(b) + IS(b)\}}{1 + I^2} = \int_0^b \{1 - E[-aI]\}\frac{S}{I}$$

or

$$\int_0^b \frac{S}{I} - A(a) = \int_0^b E[-aI]\frac{S}{I} - \int_0^a \frac{E[-bI]\{C(b) + IS(b)\}}{1 + I^2}.$$

ii. Devise a way to compute approximations to

$$\int_0^b \frac{S}{I}$$

for any positive number b. A suggestion: Start with the formula

$$\int_0^b \frac{S}{I} = \frac{\pi}{2} - C(b) \cdot \int_0^{+\infty} \frac{bE[-I]}{b^2 + I^2} - S(b) \cdot \int_0^{+\infty} \frac{IE[-I]}{b^2 + I^2},$$

a consequence of the formula in No. i.

iii. Show that

$$\int_0^{+\infty} E[-I^2] = \frac{1}{2}\sqrt{\pi}.$$

Denote this extended integral by k_0 and suppose, for each positive integer n,

$$k_n = \int_0^{+\infty} I^n \, E[-I^2] \, .$$

There is the relation, $k_n = \dfrac{n-1}{2} \cdot k_{n-2}$, $n = 2, 3, 4 \ldots$, $k_1 = \dfrac{1}{2}$.

Also, $r_n = \int_0^{\pi/2} S^n$ can be computed, $(n = 0, 1, 2 \ldots)$. Note that $k_n k_{n+2} - k_{n+1}^2 > 0$, $n = 0, 1, 2 \ldots$, inasmuch as $k_{n+2} t^2 - 2k_{n+1} t + k_n > 0$ for every number t.

Theorems

1. If the simple graph f has X-projection the interval $[a,b]$ and is of bounded variation on $[a,b]$, there exists a simple graph g nondecreasing on $[a,b]$ and a simple graph h nondecreasing on $[a,b]$ such that

$$f = g - h.$$

2. If the simple surface f has XY-projection the rectangular interval $[ab;cd]$ and is of bounded variation on $[ab;cd]$, there exists a simple surface g nondecreasing on $[ab;cd]$ and a simple surface h nondecreasing on $[ab;cd]$ such that

$$f = g - h.$$

3. If the simple graph f is nondecreasing on the interval $[a,b]$ and P is a point of f with abscissa in $[a,b]$, then f has property (Q) at the point P.

4. If the simple graph f is of bounded variation on $[a,b]$ and P a point of f with abscissa in $[a,b]$, then f has property (Q) at P.

5. If the simple graph f has X-projection $[a,b]$ and has property (Q) at each of its points then, between any two numbers x and y of $[a,b]$ there is a number z such that f is continuous at $(z,f(z))$. If f is not continuous at one of its points and M is the number set to which x belongs only if x is the abscissa of a point of f where f is not continuous, then there exists, for each positive integer n, a number set G_n containing only one number of M and such that each number of M is in G_n for some positive integer n.

6. Suppose G is a collection of segments such that each number of the interval $[a,b]$ belongs to some segment of G. Then there exists a collection H of segments such that (1) H is a finite collection, (2) each segment of H is a segment of G, and (3) each number of $[a,b]$ belongs to some segment of H.

7. Suppose M is an infinite subset of the interval $[a,b]$. There

exists a number c such that each segment containing c includes an infinite subset of M.

8. Suppose, for each positive integer n, G_n is a number set such that, if $[a,b]$ is an interval, there exists a subinterval of $[a,b]$ containing no number of G_n. If G is the set to which x belongs only if there is a positive integer n such that x belongs to G_n, then G does not fill up any interval.

9. Suppose f is a simple graph whose X-projection is the interval $[a,b]$, and, if c is a positive number, there exists a simple graph g whose X-projection is $[a,b]$, continuous at each of its points, such that $f(x)$ differs from $g(x)$ by less than c for every x in $[a,b]$. Then f is continuous at each of its points.

Successive Approximations

EXISTENCE OF CERTAIN NUMBERS ESTABLISHED BY SUCCESSIVE APPROXIMATIONS

Suppose a is a positive number and we wish to prove the existence of a positive number x whose square is a. If x_0 is any positive number, then $x_0^2 > a$, $x_0^2 = a$, or $x_0^2 < a$. In the first case, x_0 is too large and

$$x_0 > \frac{a}{x_0} \; ;$$

the average $(1/2)\{x_0 + (a/x_0)\}$ is less than x_0 and greater than (a/x_0) and may be a better approximation to the hypothetical number x whose square is a than either x_0 or (a/x_0). The same is possibly true in case $x_0^2 < a$. Thus, the number x_1, defined by

$$x_1 = \frac{1}{2}\left\{x_0 + \frac{a}{x_0}\right\} ,$$

may be a better approximation to the required number x than x_0 is. Then, x_2, defined by

$$x_2 = \frac{1}{2}\left\{x_1 + \frac{a}{x_1}\right\} ,$$

may be a still better approximation,

$$x_3 = \frac{1}{2}\left\{x_2 + \frac{a}{x_2}\right\}$$

still better, and so on.

To obtain experimental evidence in support of this conjecture, suppose a is 2 and $x_0 = 1.5$. Then,

$$x_1 = \frac{1}{2}\left\{1.5 + \frac{2}{1.5}\right\} = 1.4167.$$

Since $x_0^2 = 2.25$ and $x_1^2 = 2.007$, the conjecture is supported. Then,

$$x_2 = \frac{1}{2}\left\{1.4167 + \frac{2}{1.4167}\right\} = 1.414215$$

and $x_2^2 = 2.00004$. It appears that $x_1 > x_2$.

Lemma. If a is a positive number, x_0 a positive number, and, for each positive integer n,

$$x_n = \frac{1}{2}\left\{x_{n-1} + \frac{a}{x_{n-1}}\right\},$$

then $x_n \geq x_{n+1}$.

In fact,

$$x_n - x_{n+1} = x_n - \frac{1}{2}\left\{x_n + \frac{a}{x_n}\right\} = \frac{1}{2}\left\{x_n - \frac{a}{x_n}\right\} = \frac{1}{8x_n}\left\{x_{n-1} - \frac{a}{x_{n-1}}\right\}^2,$$

so that $x_n - x_{n+1} \geq 0$ or $x_n \geq x_{n+1}$.

Since $x_n > 0$ for every positive integer n, there is a *largest* number r which does not exceed x_n for any positive integer n. The number r is nonnegative and, if c is a positive number, there exists a number N such that x_n differs from r by less than c if $n > N$.

Now, if $\epsilon_n = x_n - r$ or $x_n = r + \epsilon_n$, then $r^2 - a = \epsilon_n^2 - 2r\epsilon_{n+1} - 2\epsilon_n\epsilon_{n+1}$. If we suppose $|r^2 - a| = c > 0$, there exists a number N such that $|\epsilon_n^2 - 2r\epsilon_{n+1} - 2\epsilon_n\epsilon_{n+1}| < c$, if $n > N$; *i.e.*, $c < c$. This contradiction shows that $r^2 = a$. Since r is nonnegative, then $r > 0$.

We have proved by "successive approximations" that there is a positive number whose square is a.

Note. Our proof shows that, for each positive integer n,

$$\epsilon_n^2 - 2r\epsilon_{n+1} - 2\epsilon_n\epsilon_{n+1} = 0,$$

i.e.,

$$\epsilon_{n+1} = \frac{\epsilon_n^2}{2(r + \epsilon_n)} < \frac{\epsilon_n^2}{2r}.$$

Thus, x_{n+1} approximates r with an error about the square of the error in the approximation of x_n to r. For instance, if x_n is accurate to k decimal places, then x_{n+1} is accurate to about $2k$ decimal places.

The problem just considered may be interpreted in the following way. Suppose f is the simple graph such that, if x is a number, $f(x) = x^2 - a$ (see figure in case $a = 2$). Since f is continuous and increasing for nonnegative abscissas, $f(0) < 0$, and $f(a + 1) > 0$, there exists only one number r such that

$$r > 0 \quad \text{and} \quad f(r) = 0.$$

Now, if x_0 is a positive number, the tangent line to f at the point $(x_0, f(x_0))$ is

$$2x_0(I - x_0) + x_0^2 - a$$

or $2x_0 I - x_0^2 - a$. The point of this straight line belonging to the horizontal line $\underline{0}$ is $(x_1, 0)$, where the

$$x_1 = \frac{1}{2}\left\{ x_0 + \frac{a}{x_0} \right\}.$$

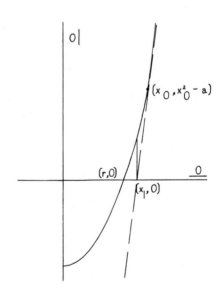

It is now geometrically evident why this method of successive approximations serves to define a number whose square is a. Moreover, the geometrical interpretation points the way to the solution of many such problems.

Exercise. If a is a positive number, x_0 a positive number, and, for each positive integer n,

$$x_n = \frac{1}{3}\left\{2x_{n-1} + \frac{a}{x_{n-1}^2}\right\},$$

then the sequence x converges to the cube root of a.

Example. If $a = 2$, $x_0 = 1.26$, then $x_1 = 1.25992$; $x_1^3 = 1.99996$.

LEMMAS CONCERNING SEQUENCES

1. Suppose k is a number and, for each positive integer n, x_n is a number such that $x_n \le x_{n+1} < k$. There exists a number r with the property that, if c is a positive number, there is a positive integer N such that, if $n > N$, then x_n differs from r by less than c, *i.e.*, the sequence x converges to the sequential limit r.

2. Suppose k is a number and, for each positive integer n, y_n is a number such that, if $y_0 = 0$,

$$\sum_{p=1}^{n} |y_p - y_{p-1}| < k.$$

There exists a number r such that the sequence y converges to r.

3. If, for each positive integer n, y_n is a number such that $|y_{n+2} - y_{n+1}| \le (1/2)|y_{n+1} - y_n|$, then there exists a number r such that the sequence y converges to r.

4. Suppose, for each positive integer n, y_n is a number such that, if c is a positive number, there exists a number N such that y_m differs from y_n by less than c if $m > N$ and $n > N$. There exists a number r such that y converges to r.

5. Suppose, for each positive integer n, f_n is a simple graph whose X-projection is the set of all numbers, continuous at each of its points and, if c is a positive number and $[a,b]$ an interval, there exists a positive integer N such that, if m and n are integers greater than N, and x a number in $[a,b]$,

$$|f_m(x) - f_n(x)| < c.$$

There exists a simple graph f whose X-projection is the set of all numbers, continuous at each of its points, such that, if c is a positive number and $[a,b]$ an interval, there exists a positive integer N such that, if n is an integer greater than N and x a number in $[a,b]$,

$$|f(x) - f_n(x)| < c.$$

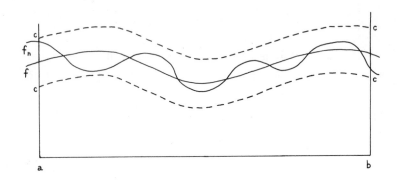

SIMPLE GRAPHS DETERMINED BY SUCCESSIVE APPROXIMATIONS

Problem. Suppose (a,b) is a point. To establish, by successive approximations, the existence of only one simple graph f whose X-projection is the set of all numbers such that f contains the point (a,b) and $f' = f$.

Theorems

1. If (a,b) is a point and f a simple graph whose X-projection is the set of all numbers, then the following two statements are equivalent:

   (i) $f(a) = b$ and $f' = f$,

and

   (ii) if x is a number, $f(x) = b + \int_a^x f$.

Note. This first theorem shows that our problem is equivalent to the problem of showing that there exists only one simple graph f for which statement (ii) is true.

2. Suppose f_0 is a simple graph whose X-projection is the set of

all numbers continuous at each of its points and, for each positive integer n and number x,

$$f_n(x) = b + \int_a^x f_{n-1} .$$

Then, f_n is continuous at each of its points and $f_{n+1}(x) - f_n(x)$ $= \int_a^x (f_n - f_{n-1})$.

3. If $[A,B]$ is an interval containing the number a, there exists a number M such that, if x is in $[A,B]$,

$$|f_1(x) - f_0(x)| \leq M,$$

and, for each positive integer n,

$$|f_{n+1}(x) - f_n(x)| \leq M \cdot \frac{|x - a|^n}{1 \cdot 2 \cdot \ldots \cdot n} .$$

4. If c is a positive number, there exists a positive integer N such that, if x is in $[A,B]$, $f_m(x)$ differs from $f_n(x)$ by less than c if $m > N$ and $n > N$.

5. There exists a simple graph f whose X-projection is the set of all numbers such that, if $[A,B]$ is an interval and c a positive number, there exists a positive integer N such that, if x is in $[A,B]$ and n an integer greater than N, then $|f(x) - f_n(x)| < c$.

6. f is continuous at each of its points.

7. If, for each positive integer n, ϵ_n is the simple graph defined by $f_n - f = \epsilon_n$, so that $f_n = f + \epsilon_n$ and if ϵ_n is continuous at each of its points, then, if x is a number,

$$f(x) - \left\{ b + \int_a^x f \right\} = \int_a^x \epsilon_{n-1} - \epsilon_n .$$

The assumption that there is a number x such that $\left| f(x) - \left\{ b + \int_a^x f \right\} \right|$ is a positive number δ leads to a contradiction so that, for every number x, $f(x) = b + \int_a^x f$.

8. If F is a simple graph whose X-projection is the set of all numbers such that, if x is a number, $F(x) = b + \int_a^x F$, then $F(x) - f(x) = \int_a^x (F - f)$ and it follows that $F = f$.

The truth of each of these statements establishes the following theorem.

Theorem. If (a,b) is a point, there exists only one simple graph f containing the point (a,b) such that, for every number x, $f'(x) = f(x)$.

Corollary. Suppose E denotes *the* simple graph f whose X-projection is the set of all numbers such that $f(0) = 1$ and $f' = f$. The following statements are true:

    i. If x is a number, $E(x) > 0$.

    ii. If x and y are numbers and $x < y$, then $E(x) < E(y)$.

    iii. If f is *the* simple graph with X-projection the set of all numbers containing the point (a,b) such that $f' = f$, then $f = bE[I - a]$.

    iv. If c is a number and x a number, $E(x + c) = E(x) \cdot E(c)$.

Theorems

1. If (a,b) is a point and g a simple graph whose X-projection is the set of all numbers, continuous at each of its points, then there exists a simple graph u such that the only simple graph f containing (a,b) for which $f' - f = g$ is $uE[I - a]$.

2. If (a,b) is a point and each of q and g a simple graph whose X-projection is the set of all numbers, continuous at each of its points, then there exists a simple graph h and a simple graph u such that the only simple graph f containing (a,b) for which $f' - qf = g$ is $uE[h - h(a)]$.

Exercise. For each nonnegative integer n, suppose E_n denotes the simple graph $E - \left\{ 1 + \dfrac{I}{1} + \dfrac{I^2}{1 \cdot 2} + \ldots + \dfrac{I^n}{1 \cdot 2 \cdot \ldots \cdot n} \right\}$. Use the preceding result to determine E_n and show that, if x is a positive number,

$$0 < E_n(x) < E(x) \cdot \frac{x^{n+1}}{1 \cdot 2 \cdot \ldots \cdot (n+1)} .$$

THE EQUATION $f' - f = -H$

Problem. Show that there is only one simple graph f whose X-projection is the set of all positive numbers such that $f' - f = -H$ and that, if α and β are horizontal lines with 0 between them, there exists a vertical line $h|$ such that every point of f to the right of $h|$ is between α and β. Show, moreover, that if x is a positive number and n a positive integer, the difference

$$f(x) - \left\{ \frac{1}{x} - 1 \cdot \left(\frac{1}{x}\right)^2 + 1 \cdot 2 \cdot \left(\frac{1}{x}\right)^3 - \ldots + (-1)^n \cdot 1 \cdot 2 \cdot \ldots \cdot n \cdot \left(\frac{1}{x}\right)^{n+1} \right\}$$

is positive or negative according as n is odd or even, and that difference is numerically less than

$$1 \cdot 2 \cdot \ \ldots \ \cdot (n + 1) \cdot \left(\frac{1}{x}\right)^{n + 2} \ ;$$

and

$$- \left(\frac{1}{x}\right)^2 < f(x) - \frac{1}{x} < 0.$$

Note. $\left| f(x) - \frac{1}{x} \right| < .005,$ if $x > 14.2$;

$\left| f(x) - \left\{ \frac{1}{x} - \left(\frac{1}{x}\right)^2 \right\} \right| < .005,$ if $x > 7.5$;

$\left| f(x) - \left\{ \frac{1}{x} - \left(\frac{1}{x}\right)^2 + 2 \cdot \left(\frac{1}{x}\right)^3 \right\} \right| < .005,$ if $x \geq 6$.

Exercise.   Devise a way to compute approximations to $f(x)$, correct to two decimal places, in the range $0 < x < 6$.

ORDERED PAIRS OF SIMPLE GRAPHS DETERMINED BY SUCCESSIVE APPROXIMATIONS

Problem.   Suppose each of a, b, and c is a number and each of q and r a simple graph with X-projection the set of all numbers, continuous at each of its points. Show that there exists *only one* ordered pair f,g, each member of which is a simple graph with X-projection the set of all numbers, such that

$$f(a) = b, \quad f' = \ \ qg,$$
$$g(a) = c, \quad g' = rf.$$

The pattern is similar to that followed in the preceding problem. The problem in question is equivalent to the problem of determining an ordered pair f,g such that, if x is a number,

$$f(x) = b + \int_a^x qg,$$

$$g(x) = c + \int_a^x rf.$$

We leave all details to the reader.

Theorem. Suppose each of a, b, and c is a number and each of q and r a simple graph with X-projection the set of all numbers, continuous at each of its points. If t is a number, denote by A_t, C_t *the* ordered pair f, g such that

$$f(t) = 1, \quad g(t) = 0, \quad f' = qg, \quad \text{and} \quad g' = rf;$$

and denote by B_t, D_t *the* ordered pair f, g such that

$$f(t) = 0, \quad g(t) = 1, \quad f' = qg, \quad \text{and} \quad g' = rf,$$

so that we have the following formulas:

$$A_t(t) = 1, \qquad B_t(t) = 0, \qquad A_t' = qC_t, \qquad B_t' = qD_t,$$
$$C_t(t) = 0, \qquad D_t(t) = 1, \qquad C_t' = rA_r, \qquad D_t' = rB_t.$$

The following statements may be established as consequences of the above definitions and the fact that there is *only one* ordered pair f, g containing the points (a, b) and (a, c), respectively, such that $f' = qg$ and $g' = rf$.

i. If t is a number, $A_t D_t - B_t C_t = \underline{1}$.

ii. The ordered pair f, g containing $\overline{(a, b)}$ and (a, c), respectively, such that $f' = qg$ and $g' = rf$, is $bA_a + cB_a$, $bC_a + cD_a$.

iii. If x, y, z is an ordered number triple,

$$A_z(x) = A_y(x)A_z(y) + B_y(x)C_z(y) \text{ and } C_z(x) = C_y(x)A_z(y) + D_y(x)C_z(y)$$

and

$$B_z(x) = A_y(x)B_z(y) + B_y(x)D_z(y) \text{ and } D_z(x) = C_y(x)B_z(y) + D_y(x)D_z(y).$$

iv. If x, t is an ordered number pair, $A_t(x) = D_x(t)$, $B_t(x) = -B_x(t)$, and $C_t(x) = -C_x(t)$.

v. If each of a, b, and c is a number and each of u and v a simple graph whose X-projection is the set of all numbers, continuous at each of its points, then the only ordered pair f, g such that $f(a) = b$, $g(a) = c$, $f' - qg = u$, and $g' - rf = v$ is given, for each number x, by

$$f(x) = bA_a(x) + cB_a(x) + \int_a^x \{uD_x - vB_x\},$$

$$g(x) = bC_a(x) + cD_a(x) + \int_a^x \{-uC_x + vA_x\}.$$

124

PARTICULAR EXAMPLES

The rest of this chapter contains outlines suggesting investigations of particular cases of the ideas of the last section.

(A). THE SIMPLE GRAPHS S AND C

Theorem. Suppose A_t, B_t, C_t, D_t is the ordered quadruple of the preceding section in case $q = \underline{-1}$ and $r = \underline{1}$, so that

$$A_t(t) = 1, \qquad B_t(t) = 0, \qquad A_t' = -C_t, \qquad B_t' = -D_t,$$

$$C_t(t) = 0, \qquad D_t(t) = 1, \qquad C_t' = A_t, \qquad D_t' = B_t.$$

The following statements are true.

i. If t is a number, $A_t = D_t$ and $B_t = -C_t$.

ii. If x, y, z is an ordered number pair:

$$A_z(x) = A_y(x)A_z(y) - B_y(x)B_z(y),$$

$$B_z(x) = A_y(x)B_z(y) + B_y(x)A_z(y).$$

iii. If h is a number, then, for every number x and number z,

$$A_{z+h}(x+h) = A_z(x),$$

$$B_{z+h}(x+h) = B_z(x).$$

That is, if x, z is an ordered number pair, x', z' is an ordered number pair, and $x' - x = z' - z$, then

$$A_{z'}(x') = A_z(x) \quad \text{and} \quad B_{z'}(x') = B_z(x).$$

This means that there is a simple graph C and a simple graph S such that, if x, t is an ordered number pair,

$$A_t(x) = C(x-t) \quad \text{and} \quad B_t(x) = S(x-t).$$

iv. $C^2 + S^2 = \underline{1}$.

v. If u is a number and v a number,

$$C(u+v) = C(u)C(v) - S(u)S(v),$$

$$S(u+v) = S(u)C(v) + C(u)S(v).$$

vi. $C' = -S$ and $S' = C$.

vii. There exists a positive number r such that $C(r) = 0$. There is a *least* such positive number r, which we denote by $(\pi/2)$.

viii. If x is a number, $C(x + 2\pi) = C(x)$ and $S(x + 2\pi) = S(x)$.

ix. Suppose, for each positive integer n,

$$S = I - \frac{I^3}{1 \cdot 2 \cdot 3} + \ldots + (-1)^{n-1} \frac{I^{2n-1}}{1 \cdot 2 \cdot \ldots (2n-1)} + S_n$$

and

$$C = 1 - \frac{I^2}{1 \cdot 2} + \frac{I^4}{1 \cdot 2 \cdot 3 \cdot 4} - \ldots + (-1)^n \frac{I^{2n}}{1 \cdot 2 \cdot \ldots \cdot (2n)} + C_n .$$

Show that

$$C_n(0) = 0, \qquad C_n' + S_n = \underline{0},$$

$$S_n(0) = 0, \qquad S_n' - C_n = (-1)^n \frac{I^{2n}}{1 \cdot 2 \cdot \ldots \cdot (2n)}$$

and hence express S_n and C_n as integrals. (See No. (v) of the preceding section.)

(B) THE EQUATION $f' = I^2 + f^2$

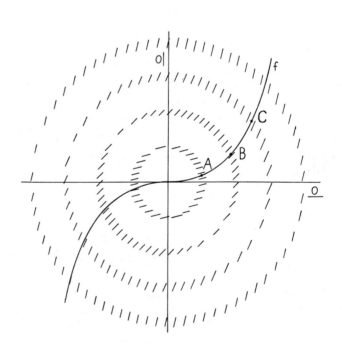

Problem. If (a,b) is a point, determine a simple graph f containing (a,b) whose X-projection is some segment containing a such that the slope of f at each of its points is the square of the radius of the circle with center $(0,0)$ which contains that point.

In the accompanying figure, (a,b) is $(0,0)$ and the simple graph f which is sketched in has slope at each of its points approximately the square of the radius of the circle with center $(0,0)$ containing that point; *e.g.*, at A the slope of f is $(1/4)$, at B 1, at C $(9/4)$ ... .

The fact that $T' = 1 + T^2$ and $T = (S/C)$ suggests, by analogy, that we try to express the simple graph f containing $(0,0)$ such that, if (x,y) is a point of f, $f'(x) = x^2 + y^2$, as the quotient (u/v) of two simple graphs. We would then have

$$\frac{vu' - uv'}{v^2} = \mathrm{I}^2 + (\frac{u}{v})^2 = \frac{\mathrm{I}^2 v^2 + u^2}{v^2}$$

and, to ensure that $f(0) = 0$:

$$u(0) = 0, \qquad v(0) = 1.$$

The conditions are met if

(i)
$$u(0) = 0, \quad u' = \quad \mathrm{I}^2 v,$$
$$v(0) = 1, \quad v' = -u.$$

This is the case $q = \mathrm{I}^2$ and $r = \underline{-1}$ of our general system. In the notation previously introduced, a simple graph f with the desired properties is the quotient $(\mathrm{B_0}/\mathrm{D_0})$ for the system (i).

Theorem. Suppose (a,b) is a point and each of q and r a simple graph with X-projection the set of all numbers, continuous at each of its points. There exists a segment s containing a such that the only simple graph f with X-projection s containing the point (a,b) for which

$$f' = q - rf^2$$

is

$$\frac{b \cdot \mathrm{A}_a + \mathrm{B}_a}{b \cdot \mathrm{C}_a + \mathrm{D}_a} \; ,$$

where $\mathrm{A}_a, \mathrm{B}_a, \mathrm{C}_a, \mathrm{D}_a$ is the ordered quadruple previously introduced (for q and r used here).

Theorem. Denote by α, β, γ, δ the ordered quadruple $\mathrm{A}_t, \mathrm{B}_t,$

C_t, D_t for the system (i) in case $t = 0$. The following statements are true.

i. For each number x,

$$\alpha(x) = 1 + \int_0^x I^2 \, \gamma, \qquad \beta(x) = \int_0^x I^2 \, \delta,$$

$$\gamma(x) = -\int_0^x \alpha, \qquad \delta(x) = 1 - \int_0^x \beta.$$

ii. If t is a number,

$$A_t = \alpha \cdot \delta(t) - \beta \cdot \gamma(t), \qquad B_t = \gamma \cdot \delta(t) - \delta \cdot \gamma(t),$$

$$C_t = \beta \cdot \alpha(t) - \alpha \cdot \beta(t), \qquad D_t = \delta \cdot \alpha(t) - \gamma \cdot \beta(t).$$

iii. If n is a positive integer,

$$\alpha = 1 - \frac{I^4}{1 \cdot 4} + \frac{I^8}{(1 \cdot 4)(5 \cdot 8)} - \frac{I^{12}}{(1 \cdot 4)(5 \cdot 8)(9 \cdot 12)} + \cdots$$

$$+ (-1)^n \frac{I^{4n}}{(1 \cdot 4)(5 \cdot 8) \ldots ([4n - 3][4n])} + \alpha_n,$$

where, if x is a number distinct from 0 and n a positive integer such that

$$\frac{x^4}{(4n - 3)(4n)} < 1,$$

$$|\alpha(x) - \alpha_n(x)| < \frac{x^{4n + 4}}{(1 \cdot 4)(5 \cdot 8) \ldots ([4n + 1][4n + 4])}.$$

With an analogous estimate for the "error" in each case, there are the following formulas:

$$\beta = \frac{I^3}{3} - \frac{I^7}{3(4 \cdot 7)} + \frac{I^{11}}{3(4 \cdot 7)(8 \cdot 11)} - \frac{I^{15}}{3(4 \cdot 7)(8 \cdot 11)(12 \cdot 15)} + \cdots$$

$$+ (-1)^n \frac{I^{4n + 3}}{3(4 \cdot 7)(8 \cdot 11) \ldots (4n[4n + 3])} + \beta_n ;$$

$$\gamma = -I + \frac{I^5}{4 \cdot 5} - \frac{I^9}{(4 \cdot 5)(8 \cdot 9)} + \frac{I^{13}}{(4 \cdot 5)(8 \cdot 9)(12 \cdot 13)} - \cdots$$

$$+ (-1)^{n - 1} \frac{I^{4n + 1}}{(4 \cdot 5)(8 \cdot 9) \ldots (4n[4n + 1])} + \gamma_n ;$$

$$\delta = 1 - \frac{I^4}{(3\cdot 4)} + \frac{I^8}{(3\cdot 4)(7\cdot 8)} - \frac{I^{12}}{(3\cdot 4)(7\cdot 8)(11\cdot 12)} + \cdots$$

$$+ (-1)^n \frac{I^{4n}}{(3\cdot 4)(7\cdot 8)\ \ldots\ ([4n-1][4n])} + \delta_n .$$

Exercise. The simple graph f of the last figure, such that $f(0) = 0$ and $f' = I^2 + f^2$ is (β/δ), (restricted to a segment about 0).

i. Show that $f(1) = .35023$, to five decimal places.

ii. Show that $\delta(2) = .004$. The least positive number r such that $\delta(r) = 0$ is approximately 2. A better approximation to r is 2.00314. The X-projection of the simple graph f is the set of all numbers between $-r$ and r.

iii. Indicate a way to compute points of the simple graph f containing the point (a,b) such that $f' = I^2 + f^2$.

iv. Show that $\delta'' + I^2 \delta = \underline{0}$, $\gamma'' + I^2\gamma = \underline{0}$, $\gamma\delta' - \delta\gamma' = \underline{1}$.

v. Suppose each of a, $\bar{b}$, and c is a number and each of p, q, r, and s a simple graph with X-projection the set of all numbers, continuous at each of its points. Define h and k by

$$h(x) = -\int_a^x p \quad \text{and} \quad k(x) = -\int_a^x s,$$

and F and G by

$$F = E[h] \cdot f \quad \text{and} \quad G = E[k] \cdot g,$$

and q_1 and r_1 by

$$q_1 = q \cdot E[h-k] \quad \text{and} \quad r_1 = r \cdot E[k-h].$$

The following two statements are equivalent:

(i) $f(a) = b$, $g(a) = c$, $f' = pf + qg$, $g' = rf + sg$,

and

(ii) $F(a) = b$, $G(a) = c$, $F' = q_1 G$, and $G' = r_1 F$.

Thus, the solution of the system (i) is equivalent to the solution of the system (ii).

(C) THE EQUATION $uf'' + vf' + wf = g$

Problem. Suppose each of u, v, w, and g is a simple graph whose X-projection is the set of all numbers, continuous at each of its points and, if x is a number, $u(x) > 0$. If each of a, b, and c is a number, determine a simple graph f such that $f(a) = b$, $f'(a) = c$, and $uf'' + vf' + wf = g$.

Theorems. The following statements are true under the conditions just stated.

1. There exists a simple graph m, continuous at each of its points, such that, if x is a number, $m(x) > 0$; a simple graph p, continuous at each of its points, such that, if x is a number, $p(x) > 0$, and a simple graph q continuous at $(x, q(x))$ for every number x, such that, for appropriate f,

$$m\{uf'' + vf' + wf\} = \{pf'\}' - qf,$$

so that the equation of the above problem may be replaced by the equation

$$\{pf'\}' - qf = mg.$$

2. The last equation, together with the conditions $f(a) = b$, $f'(a) = c$, is a system equivalent to the system,

$$f(a) = b, \qquad\qquad f' = \frac{1}{p} \cdot g,$$

$$g(a) = cp(a), \qquad\qquad g' = q \cdot f + mg,$$

which is a particular case of the system considered in the preceding sections.

3. Suppose each of f and g is a simple graph, $f'' - qf = \underline{0}$ and $g'' - qg = 0$. The following statements are true.

i. There exists a number c such that $fg' - gf' = \underline{c}$.

ii. If $c \neq 0$, then, if x is a number,

$$|f(x)| + |g(x)| > 0,$$
$$|f'(x)| + |g'(x)| > 0,$$
$$|f(x)| + |f'(x)| > 0.$$

iii. If $c \neq 0$ and M is the number set to which x belongs only if $f(x) = 0$, then no interval includes an infinite subset of M.

iv. If $c \neq 0$ and h, k is an ordered number pair such that $hf + kg = 0$, then $h = 0$ and $k = 0$.

v. If $c = 0$, there exists a number k such that $f = kg$, or a number k such that $g = kf$.

vi. If $c \neq 0$ and r and s are numbers such that $f(r) = 0$, $f(s) = 0$, and, if x is between r and s, $f(x) \neq 0$, then there exists only one number t between r and s such that $g(t) = 0$.

vii. If Q is a continuous simple graph such that $Q(x) \geq q(x)$ for every number x and each segment contains a number x such that $Q(x) > q(x)$, if $f'' + qf = 0$, $F'' + QF = 0$, and r and s are numbers such that $f(r) = 0$ and $\overline{f}(s) = 0$, then there is a number t between r and s such that $F(t) = 0$.

Linear Spaces of Simple Graphs

In this chapter, we first outline some selected theorems about the "space of points," *i.e.*, the "plane" of ordered number pairs, and then undertake to lead the reader to extend these theorems to a "space" in which the word "point" is interpreted to mean "continuous simple graph with X-projection the interval $[a,b]$," *i.e.*, a space in which "point" means a certain kind of set of ordinary points.

LINEAR TRANSFORMATIONS IN THE PLANE

To make the proposed extension or generalization easier to accomplish, we introduce some changes in the notation hitherto used.

If f is a point, *i.e.*, an ordered number pair, we denote the point by $(f(1),f(2))$. (A *point* f is determined by $f(x)$, $x = 1,2$, while a simple graph with X-projection $[a,b]$ is determined by $f(x)$, $a \leq x \leq b$.)

Definition. The statement that the transformation W from the set of all points to a point set *is linear* means that, if f is a point, g a point, and k a number, then

$$W(f + g) = Wf + Wg \quad \text{and} \quad W(k \cdot f) = k \cdot Wf.$$

(See the definitions of *sum*, *product by a number*, *inner product*, and *absolute value*, for points, on pages 69-70.)

Theorems. Suppose W is a transformation from the set of all points to a point set.

1. The following two statements are equivalent:
    (i) W is linear,

and

(ii) there exists a transformation K from the set of four points $\{(1,1), (1,2), (2,1), (2,2)\}$ to a number set such that, if h is a point and $f = Wh$, then

$$f(x) = \sum_{y=1}^{2} K(x,y)h(y), \quad (x = 1,2).$$

2. If W is linear, then, either there exists a point f distinct from $(0,0)$ such that $Wf = (0,0)$, or, if g is a point, there exists only one point f such that $Wf = g$.

3. If W is linear and reversible and $K(1,2) = K(2,1)$, *i.e.*, K *is symmetric*, then there exists an ordered number pair λ_1, λ_2 and an ordered point pair ϕ_1, ϕ_2 such that

(i) $|\phi_1| = 1$, $|\phi_2| = 1$ and $(\!(\phi_1, \phi_2)\!) = 0$,

and

(ii) $\phi_1 = \lambda_1 \cdot W\phi_1$ and $\phi_2 = \lambda_2 \cdot W\phi_2$.

Moreover,

$$K(x,y) = \sum_{p=1}^{2} \frac{\phi_p(x)\phi_p(y)}{\lambda_p}, \quad (x = 1,2; \; y = 1,2);$$

and, if ϕ is a point,

$$\phi = \sum_{p=1}^{2} (\!(\phi, \phi_p)\!) \cdot \phi_p.$$

Example. If $K(1,1) = 5$, $K(1,2) = K(2,1) = 2$, and $K(2,2) = 2$, then $\lambda_1 = 1$, $\lambda_2 = \frac{1}{6}$, $\phi_1 = \left(-\frac{1}{\sqrt{5}}, \frac{2}{\sqrt{5}}\right)$, and $\phi_2 = \left(\frac{2}{\sqrt{5}}, \frac{1}{\sqrt{5}}\right)$. On the other hand, if $K(1,1) = 1$, $K(1,2) = K(2,1) = 0$, and $K(2,2) = 1$, then $\lambda_1 = \lambda_2 = 1$, $\phi_1 = \left(\frac{3}{5}, \frac{4}{5}\right)$, and $\phi_2 = \left(\frac{4}{5}, -\frac{3}{5}\right)$ (and any other point pair satisfying (i) of No. 3 (above)).

AXIOMS FOR LINEAR SPACE

The statement that S is a *linear space* means that S consists of a point set, where the word *point* is undefined, in which there is an addition and a multiplication by numbers satisfying the following axioms.

Axiom I.

    i. If f is a point, and g a point, there is only one point $f + g$ (called the *sum* of f and g).

    ii. If each of f, g, and h is a point, then

$$f + (g + h) = (f + g) + h.$$

    iii. If f is a point and g a point, then

$$f + g = g + f.$$

    iv. There is a point N such that, if f is a point,

$$N + f = f.$$

Axiom II.

    i. If f is a point and k a number, there is only one point $k \cdot f$ (called the *product k dot f*).

    ii. If each of f and g is a point and k a number,

$$k \cdot (f + g) = k \cdot f + k \cdot g.$$

    iii. If each of k_1 and k_2 is a number and f a point,

$$k_1 \cdot (k_2 \cdot f) = (k_1 k_2) \cdot f.$$

    iv. If each of k_1 and k_2 is a number and f a point,

$$(k_1 + k_2) \cdot f = k_1 \cdot f + k_2 \cdot f.$$

Axiom III.

If k is a number and f a point, then the following two statements are equivalent:

    i. $k \cdot f = N$,

and

    ii. $k = 0$ or $f = N$.

Theorems

1. If N' is a point such that, for every point f,

$$N' + f = f,$$

then $N' = N$.

2. If f is a point, then

$$1 \cdot f = f.$$

The point N is called the *zero point* of S.

The point $-1 \cdot f$ is denoted by $-f$ and called the *negative* of the point f. We have

$$f + (-f) = 1 \cdot f + (-1) \cdot f = [1 + (-1)] \cdot f = 0 \cdot f = \mathrm{N}.$$

If each of f and g is a point, the point $f + (-g)$ is denoted by $f - g$ and called the *difference f minus g*. In particular, $f - f = \mathrm{N}$.

The statement that S is a *normed* linear space, means that S is a linear space such that, for each point f, there is a number $\|f\|$ (called the *norm* of f) such that

   i. if f is a point, $\|f\| > 0$ unless $f = \mathrm{N}$;

   ii. if f is a point and k a number, then $\|k \cdot f\| = |k| \, \|f\|$; and

   iii. if each of f and g is a point, then

$$\|f + g\| \leq \|f\| + \|g\|.$$

If f is a point and g a point, $\|f - g\|$ is the *distance* from f to g. Distance has the properties,

   i. if each of f and g is a point, $\|f - g\| = \|g - f\|$ and $\|f - g\| > 0$ unless $f = g$;

   ii. if each of f and g is a point and k a number, then

$$\|k \cdot f - k \cdot g\| = |k| \, \|f - g\| ;$$

and

   iii. if each of f, g, and h is a point, then

$$\|f - h\| \leq \|f - g\| + \|g - h\|. \, .$$

The statement that S is an *inner product* space means that S is a linear space such that, for each point f and point g there is a number $(\!(f,g)\!)$ (called the inner product of f and g) such that,

   i. if each of f and g is a point, $(\!(f,g)\!)$ is a number and $(\!(f,f)\!) > 0$ unless $f = \mathrm{N}$;

   ii. if each of f and g is a point, then

$$(\!(f,g)\!) = (\!(g,f)\!) ;$$

   iii. if each of f and g is a point and k a number, then

$$(\!(k \cdot f,g)\!) = k (\!(f,g)\!) ;$$

and

   iv. if each of f, g, and h is a point, then

$$(\!(f + g, h)\!) = (\!(f, h)\!) + (\!(g, h)\!).$$

Theorem.   If each of f and g is a point, then

$$((f,g))^2 \leq ((f,f))((g,g)).$$

The inner product space is a normed linear space with the norm of the point f given by

$$\|f\| = ((f,f))^{1/2} .$$

Examples

1. The space S in which *point* means *number*, with ordinary addition and multiplication, is an inner product space with the inner product the ordinary product.

2. The plane in which *point* means ordered number pair, with ordinary addition and multiplication by numbers, is an inner product space if inner product is defined as on page 69.

3. The space in which *point* means simple graph with X-projection the interval $[a,b]$, with ordinary addition and multiplication by numbers, is a linear space.

THE INNER PRODUCT SPACE $M[a,b]$

Throughout the rest of this chapter, the simple graphs considered have X-projection an interval or, in one case, a segment. We shall agree that a familiar symbol for a particular simple graph, *e.g.*, I, L, E, S, K, $\underline{k}$, shall represent the subset of the simple graph formerly represented by that symbol whose X-projection is the interval or segment used. For instance, if the interval $[0,1]$ is the X-projection of all simple graphs used in a certain discussion then, in that discussion, $\underline{0}$ denotes the simple graph with X-projection $[0,1]$ such that, if x is in $[0,1]$, $f(x) = 0$.

Definition. $M[a,b]$ denotes the inner product space in which *point* means continuous simple graph with X-projection the interval $[a,b]$ with inner product defined by

$$((f,g)) = \int_a^b fg,$$

for every f and g in $M[a,b]$. The *norm* is then $\left\{ \int_a^b f^2 \right\}^{1/2} = \|f\|$, and the *distance* from f to g is $\|f - g\|$.

SOME LINEAR TRANSFORMATIONS IN $M[a,b]$

Suppose each of p and q is a continuous simple graph with X-projection $[a,b]$ and, if x is in $[a,b]$,

$$p(x) > 0.$$

Denote by $M_0[a,b]$ the inner product space in which *point* means an f belonging to $M[a,b]$ such that

$$f(a) = 0, \quad f(b) = 0$$

and

$$qf - \{pf'\}'$$

belongs to $M[a,b]$, with the inner product defined in $M[a,b]$; *i.e.*, $M_0[a,b]$ is a *sub-space* of $M[a,b]$.

The transformation V from $M_0[a,b]$ to a point set of $M[a,b]$ defined, for each f in $M_0[a,b]$, by

$$Vf = qf - \{pf'\}'$$

is *linear*; *i.e.*, if f is in $M_0[a,b]$, g in $M_0[a,b]$ and k a number, then

$$V(f + g) = Vf + Vg, \quad \text{and} \quad V(k \cdot f) = k \cdot Vf.$$

By merely restricting all simple graphs considered to have X-projection $[a,b]$, we have from the work of the preceding chapter, for each t in $[a,b]$, the ordered quadruple A_t, B_t, C_t, D_t, each a simple graph with X-projection $[a,b]$, defined by

$$A_t(t) = 1, \quad B_t(t) = 0, \quad A_t' = \frac{1}{p}C_t, \quad B_t' = \frac{1}{p}D_t,$$
$$C_t(t) = 0, \quad D_t(t) = 1, \quad C_t' = qA_t, \quad D_t' = qB_t.$$

We state the formulas for convenience in reference:

$$A_t D_t - B_t C_t = \underline{1},$$

$$A_t(x) = D_x(t), \quad B_t(x) = -B_x(t), \quad \text{and} \quad C_t(x) = -C_x(t),$$

$$A_y(x) = A_t(x)A_y(t) + B_t(x)C_y(t),$$
$$C_y(x) = C_t(x)A_y(t) + D_t(x)C_y(t),$$
$$B_y(x) = A_t(x)B_y(t) + B_t(x)D_y(t),$$
$$D_y(x) = C_t(x)B_y(t) + D_t(x)D_y(t).$$

Also:

$$VA_t = \underline{0}, \quad A_t(t) = 1, \quad A_t'(t) = 0,$$
$$VB_t = \underline{0}, \quad B_t(t) = 0, \quad p(t)B_t'(t) = 1.$$

Theorem. There are two alternatives; either,

i. there exists a point f in $M_0[a,b]$, distinct from $\underline{0}$, such that $Vf = \underline{0}$, or,

ii. if h is in $M[a,b]$, there exists only one f in $M_0[a,b]$ such that $V_f = h$.

The first alternative occurs in case $B_a(b) = 0$ and the second in case $B_a(b) \neq 0$. In the second alternative, V is a reversible transformation from $M_0[a,b]$ to $M[a,b]$. If W is the inverse of the transformation V and h is in $M[a,b]$, then the only f in $M_0[a,b]$ such that $Vf = h$, i.e., Wh, is given by

$$f(x) = \int_a^b K[x,I]h, \qquad a \leq x \leq b,$$

where K is the transformation from $[ab;ab]$ to a number set defined by

$$K(x,y) = \begin{cases} \dfrac{B_a(x)B_b(y)}{B_b(a)}, & \text{if } a \leq x \leq y \leq b, \\[2ex] \dfrac{B_a(y)B_b(x)}{B_b(a)}, & \text{if } a \leq y \leq x \leq b. \end{cases}$$

K is called the *kernel* of the transformation W. Note that K is *symmetric*; i.e., if (x,y) is in $[ab;ab]$, $K(x,y) = K(y,x)$.

Exercise. In case $[a,b] = [0,1]$, $Vf = -f''$, show that the second alternative is the case and that

$$K(x,y) = \begin{cases} x(1-y), & \text{if } 0 \leq x \leq y \leq 1, \\[2ex] y(1-x), & \text{if } 0 \leq y \leq x \leq 1. \end{cases}$$

RECIPE FOR THE KERNEL

We first state a formula which furnishes a key to other problems of the kind just considered.

Theorem. Suppose f and g are simple graphs such that Vf and Vg are integrable on the subinterval $[s,t]$ of $[a,b]$. Then

$$\int_s^t \{gVf - fVg\} = \{p(fg' - gf')\}\big|_s^t .$$

The simple graphs f which are the "points" of the space $M_0[a,b]$ are required to satisfy the *end-point* conditions, $f(a) = 0$, $f(b) = 0$. Denote by c a pair of end-point conditions such that, if f and g are simple graphs with X-projection $[a,b]$ satisfying the end-point conditions c, then

$$\{p(fg' - gf')\}|_a^b = 0;$$

and denote by $M_c[a,b]$ the subspace of $M[a,b]$ defined in the same way $M_0[a,b]$ was defined *except* with conditions c instead of with the conditions, $f(a) = 0$, $f(b) = 0$.

Examples of admissible end-point conditions are,

$$f'(a) = 0, \quad f'(b) = 0;$$

and

$$f(a) = -f(b), \quad p(a)f'(a) = -p(b)f'(b).$$

Definition. The statement that K is a *kernel* of the transformation V under the end-point conditions c means that K is a transformation from $[ab; ab]$ to a number set such that, if y is a number between a and b, u the subset of $K[I,y]$ with X-projection $[a,y]$, and v the subset of $K[I,y]$ with X-projection $[y,b]$, then

    i. $Vu = \underline{0}$ and $Vv = \underline{0}$,

    ii. $u'(y) - v'(y) = \dfrac{1}{p(y)}$,

    iii. $K[I,y]$ is continuous,

and

    iv. $K[I,y]$ satisfies the end-point conditions c.

Note. This "recipe for K" may be stated in what is perhaps a self-explanatory notation as follows:

    i. $VK[I,y] = \underline{0}$ on $[a,y]$ and on $[y,b]$,

    ii. $K_1'(y-,y) - K_1'(y+,y) = \dfrac{1}{p(y)}$,

    iii. $K(y-,y) = K(y+,y)$,

and

    iv. $K[I,y]$ satisfies conditions c.

Example. Let us construct K according to the recipe in case $[a,b] = [0,1]$, $Vf = -f''$, and c is $f(0) = 0$, $f(1) = 0$.

If y is a number between 0 and 1, then, by (i):

$$K(x,y) = \begin{cases} c_1 x + c_2, & \text{if } 0 \le x \le y, \\ c_3 x + c_4, & \text{if } y \le x \le 1, \end{cases}$$

where each of $c_1,$ $c_2,$ $c_3,$ and c_4 is a number. By (ii),

$$c_1 - c_3 = 1;$$

by (iii),

$$c_1 y + c_2 = c_3 y + c_4 \, ;$$

and by (iv),

$$c_2 = 0 \quad \text{and} \quad c_3 + c_4 = 0.$$

These four equations determine c_1, c_2, c_3, c_4:

$$c_1 = 1 - y, \qquad c_2 = 0, \qquad c_3 = -y, \qquad c_4 = y,$$

and consequently,

$$K(x,y) = \begin{cases} x(1-y), & \text{if } 0 \le x \le y, \\ y(1-x), & \text{if } y \le x \le 1. \end{cases}$$

Theorem. Suppose each of K and k is a kernel of the transformation V under the end-point conditions c. The following statements are true.

    i. If (x,y) is a point interior to $[ab;ab]$, then

$$K(x,y) = k(y,x),$$

K is symmetric; *i.e.*, $K(x,y) = K(y,x)$, and $k = K$.

    ii. If h is in $M[a,b]$ and, if there is an f in $M_c[a,b]$ such that $Vf = h$, then

$$f(x) = \int_a^b K[x,\mathrm{I}]h, \qquad a \le x \le b.$$

Exercise. Suppose $Vf = -f''$. In each of the following, find the kernel of V under the stated end-point conditions:

    i. $[a,b] = [0,1]$, $f(0) = 0$, $f'(1) = 0$,

    ii. $[a,b] = [-1,1]$, $f(-1) = 0$, $f(1) = 0$,

    iii. $[a,b] = [0,1]$, $f(0) = -f(1)$, $f'(0) = -f'(1)$.

In each case, V is a reversible transformation from $M_c[a,b]$ to $M[a,b]$ with inverse transformation defined by

$$f(x) = \int_a^b K[x,\mathrm{I}]h, \qquad a \le x \le b.$$

Suppose c is a pair of end-point conditions such that, in addition to the conditions already imposed, if f satisfies c, then $pff'|_a^b = 0$, and suppose V is a reversible transformation from $M_c[a,b]$ to $M[a,b]$, with kernel K. If h is in $M[a,b]$ and $Vf = h$, then

$$\int_a^b \int_a^b K(x,y)h(x)h(y)dxdy = \int_a^b \{pf'^2 + qf^2\}.$$

Note. This formula shows that, if $q(x) \geq 0$ for every x in $[a,b]$, then $\int_a^b \int_a^b K(x,y)h(x)h(y)dxdy \geq 0$ for every h in $M[a,b]$.

ANOTHER KIND OF END-POINT PROBLEM

Denote by $M(-1,1)$ the linear space in which *point* means continuous simple graph with X-projection the segment Δ with ends -1 and 1 and by $M_1(-1,1)$ the subspace of $M(-1,1)$ in which *point* means an f in $M(-1,1)$ such that f'' is continuous and has X-projection the segment Δ.

If we restrict all simple graphs considered to have X-projection Δ, the earlier investigations show that, for t in Δ, there is an ordered quadruple A_t, B_t, C_t, D_t defined by

$$A_t(t) = 1, \quad B_t(t) = 0, \quad A_t' = \frac{1}{1-I^2}C_t, \quad B_t' = \frac{1}{1-I^2}D_t,$$

$$C_t(t) = 0, \quad D_t(t) = 1, \quad C_t' = \underline{0}, \quad D_t' = \underline{1},$$

namely:

$$A_t = \underline{1}, \quad B_t = \frac{1}{2}L\left[\frac{(1+I)(1-t)}{(1+t)(1-I)}\right], \quad C_t = \underline{0}, \quad \text{and} \quad D_t = \underline{1}.$$

If each of a, b, and c is a number and a is in Δ, there exists, for each h in $M(-1,1)$, only one f in $M_1(-1,1)$ such that

$$f(a) = b, \quad f'(a) = c, \quad \text{and} \quad -\{(1-I^2)f'\}' = h.$$

Thus, the transformation Z defined, for each f in $M_1(-1,1)$, by

$$Zf = -\{(1-I^2)f'\}'$$

is a transformation from $M_1(-1,1)$ to $M(-1,1)$.

Problem. Find a subspace G of $M(-1,1)$ and a subspace G_1 of $M_1(-1,1)$ such that Z is a reversible transformation from G_1 to G.

Note 1. If f is in $M(-1,1)$ and has derivative f' bounded on the common part of Δ and a segment containing -1, and on the common part of Δ and a segment containing 1, then f is bounded on Δ and, in fact, there exists a point with abscissa -1 and a point with abscissa 1 such that, if these two points are added to f, the extended simple graph with X-projection the interval $[-1,1]$ is continuous at each of its points.

Note 2. If h is in $M(-1,1)$ and f in $M_1(-1,1)$ and $Zf = h$, then, under the hypothesis that f' is bounded on the segment Δ, if c is a positive number, there exists a positive number δ such that, if $[u,v]$ is an interval such that

$$-1 < u < -1 + \delta, \quad \text{and} \quad 1 - \delta < v < 1,$$

then $\left| \int_u^v h \right| < c$. That is, the extended integral

$$\int_{-1}^1 h = 0.$$

Note 3. If h is in $M(-1,1)$ and f in $M_1(-1,1)$ and $Zf = h$, then $f + \underline{1}$ is in $M_1(-1,1)$ and $Z(f + \underline{1}) = h$. This suggests that we impose upon f some such condition as $\int_{-1}^1 f = 0$.

Suggestion. Denote by G the subspace of $M(-1,1)$ in which point means an h in $M(-1,1)$ which is bounded on the segment Δ such that $\int_{-1}^1 h = 0$; and by G_1 the subspace of $M_1(-1,1)$ in which point means an f in $M_1(-1,1)$ such that f' is bounded on Δ and $\int_{-1}^1 f = 0$. Perhaps the transformation Z is a reversible transformation from G_1 to G.

SIMPLE KERNELS

The statement that K is a *simple kernel* means that K is a simple surface with XY-projection a rectangular interval $[ab;ab]$ which is *symmetric*, i.e., $K(x,y) = K(y,x)$ for every x and y in $[a,b]$, *continuous*, and, for some point P in $[ab;ab]$, $K(P) \neq 0$. If h is in $M[a,b]$, the simple graph f, defined by means of the simple kernel K as follows,

$$f(x) = \int_a^b K[x,I]h, \quad a \leq x \leq b,$$

is in $M[a,b]$. In fact, this formula defines a linear transformation from $M[a,b]$ to a subset of $M[a,b]$. We use the letter K to denote both the simple kernel and this transformation:

$$f = Kh.$$

Note that, if each of u and v is in $M[a,b]$, then

$$((Ku,v)) = ((u,Kv)).$$

Definition. The statement that λ is a *proper value* of the simple kernel K and ϕ a *proper function* of K belonging to λ, means that λ is a number, ϕ is in $M[a,b]$ and is distinct from $\underline{0}$, and

$$\phi = \lambda \cdot K\phi.$$

Theorem. If λ_1 and λ_2 are proper values of the simple kernel K, and ϕ_1 and ϕ_2 are proper functions of K belonging to λ_1 and λ_2, respectively, then $(\!(\phi_1, \phi_2)\!) = 0$.

Definition. The statement that the element f of $M[a,b]$ is *orthogonal* to the element g of $M[a,b]$ means that

$$(\!(f,g)\!) = 0.$$

The set S of elements of $M[a,b]$ is an *orthonormal* set in case each f in S has norm 1 and each two elements of S are orthogonal to one another.

Exercises

1. Show that if $K(x,y) = xy$, for every point (x,y) in $[01;01]$, then K has just one proper value.

2. Show that if $K(x,y) = x + y$ for every point (x,y) in $[01;01]$, then K has just two proper values.

3. If K is the simple kernel whose XY-projection is $[01;01]$, defined by

$$K(x,y) = \begin{cases} x(1-y), & \text{if } 0 \le x \le y \le 1, \\ y(1-x), & \text{if } 0 \le y \le x \le 1, \end{cases}$$

then λ is a proper value of K and ϕ a proper function of K belonging to λ only if λ is a number and ϕ an element of $M[0,1]$ such that $\phi \ne \underline{0}$, $\phi(0) = 0$, $\phi(1) = 0$, and $\phi'' = -\lambda \cdot \phi$. Hence show that the proper values of K are

$$\lambda_p = \pi^2 p^2, \quad p = 1,2,3 \ldots ,$$

and that the simple graph ϕ is a proper function of K belonging to λ_p only if ϕ is a product $k \cdot \phi_p$, where k is a number distinct from 0 and

$$\phi_p = \sqrt{2} \cdot S[\pi p I], \quad (p = 1,2,3 \ldots).$$

Note. The factor $\sqrt{2}$ is introduced in order that $\|\phi_p\| = 1$. Thus, ϕ_p, $p = 1,2,3 \ldots$, is an orthonormal set.

4. Suppose $Vf = -f''$ and c is the pair of end-point conditions

$$f(0) = -f(1), \quad f'(0) = -f'(1).$$

Show that the kernel of V under c is

$$K(x,y) = \begin{cases} \dfrac{1}{2}(x - y) + \dfrac{1}{4}, & \text{if } 0 \le x \le y \le 1, \\[2mm] \dfrac{1}{2}(y - x) + \dfrac{1}{4}, & \text{if } 0 \le y \le x \le 1. \end{cases}$$

The proper values of K are

$$\lambda_p = (2p - 1)^2 \pi^2, \quad p = 1,2 \ldots ,$$

and ϕ is a proper function of K belonging to λ_p only if there exists an ordered number pair k_1, k_2 such that $k_1 \ne 0$ or $k_2 \ne 0$ and $\phi = k_1 C[(2p - 1)\pi I] + k_2 S[(2p - 1)\pi I]$.

5. Suppose $\phi_1 \ldots \phi_n$ is a finite orthonormal subset of $M[a,b]$ and each of $\lambda_1 \ldots \lambda_n$ is a number distinct from 0. If K is the simple graph in space with XY-projection $[ab; ab]$ defined by

$$K(x,y) = \sum_{p=1}^{n} \frac{\phi_p(x)\phi_p(y)}{\lambda_p}, \quad a \le \frac{x}{y} \le b,$$

then the following statements are true:

(i) K is a simple kernel;

(ii) λ is a proper value of K only if there is a positive integer p not greater than n such that $\lambda = \lambda_p$;

(iii) ϕ is a proper function of K belonging to the proper value λ of K only if there exists an ordered number n-tuple $k_1 \ldots k_n$ such that $|k_1| + \ldots + |k_n| > 0$, $\phi = k_1 \phi_1 + \ldots + k_n \phi_n$, and $k_p = 0$ for each positive integer p not greater than n such that $\lambda_p \ne \lambda$.

Theorem. If K is a simple kernel, then K has a proper value.

We suggest that the reader take this theorem for granted for the present and use it as an axiom in the investigations. The symmetry of K is essential. For instance, if $K(x,y) = S(x) \cdot C(y)$ and $[a,b]$ is $[0, 2\pi]$, there is no proper value.

AN IDENTITY AND SOME CONSEQUENCES

Suppose $\phi_1 \ldots \phi_n$ is a finite orthonormal subset of $M[a,b]$, f a point of $M[a,b]$ and $k_1 \ldots k_n$ a number n-tuple. Then

$$\left\| f - \sum_{p=1}^{n} k_p \cdot \phi_p \right\|^2 = \|f\|^2 - \sum_{p=1}^{n} ((f, \phi_p))^2 + \sum_{p=1}^{n} \{((f, \phi_{p\text{I}})) - k_p\}^2.$$

From this identity, there follow the subsequent statements:

i. $\left\| f - \sum_{p=1}^{n} k_p \cdot \phi_p \right\| > \left\| f - \sum_{p=1}^{n} ((f, \phi_p)) \cdot \phi_p \right\|$ unless $k_p = ((f, \phi_p))$,

$p = 1 \ldots n$;

ii. $\sum_{p=1}^{n} ((f, \phi_p))^2 \leq \|f\|^2$; and

iii. if ϕ_p is a proper function of the simple kernel K belonging to the proper value λ_p, $p = 1 \ldots n$, then

$$\sum_{p=1}^{n} \left(\frac{1}{\lambda_p}\right)^2 \leq \int_a^b \int_a^b \{K(x,y)\}^2 \, dx \, dy.$$

Consequently,
   (a) no interval includes an infinite set of proper values of K,
   (b) if m of the ϕ_p belong to the same proper value λ of K, then

$$m \leq \lambda^2 \int_a^b \int_a^b \{K(x,y)\} \, dx \, dy ,$$

   (c) if the set of proper values of the simple kernel K is an infinite set M, there exists a number sequence $\{\lambda_p\}_{p=1}^{\infty}$ such that λ is a proper value of K only if there is a positive integer p such that $\lambda = \lambda_p$; and $|\lambda_p| \leq |\lambda_{p+1}|$ for every positive integer p.

SOME "GEOMETRY" IN THE SPACE M[a,b]

Suppose $f_1 \ldots f_n$ are n points of M[a,b] such that, if $k_1 \ldots k_n$ is a number n-tuple and $k_1 \cdot f_1 + \ldots + k_n \cdot f_n = 0$, then $k_1 = \ldots = k_n = 0$. Denote by R the point set in H[a,b] to which f belongs only if there exists a number n-tuple $k_1 \ldots k_n$ such that $f = k_1 \cdot f_1 + \ldots + k_n \cdot f_n$. R is the point set of a linear subspace of M[a,b] which may be called an *n-plane* in M[a,b].

Theorem. If g is a point of M[a,b], there exists a point f in the n-plane R which is nearer g than any other point of R:

$$\|g - f\| < \left\| g - \sum_{p=1}^{n} k_p \cdot f_p \right\|$$

unless $f = \sum_{p=1}^{n} k_p \cdot f_p$.

Suggestion.   Settle this first in case $f_1 \ldots f_n$ is an orthonormal set.

COMPLETE ORTHONORMAL SETS

Definition.   The statement that the subset S of $M[a,b]$ is a complete orthonormal set of proper functions of the simple kernel K means that each f in S is a proper function of K, that S is an orthonormal set, and that, if ϕ is a proper function of K, there exists a number n-tuple $k_1 \ldots k_n$ such that

$$\phi = \sum_{p=1}^{n} k_p \cdot \phi_p .$$

Theorem.   If K is a simple kernel, then K has a complete orthonormal set S of proper functions which is a finite set or an infinite set which is an infinite sequence $\{\phi_p\}_{p=1}^{\infty}$ such that ϕ belongs to S only if there exists a positive integer p for which $\phi = \phi_p$.

THE FIRST EXPANSION THEOREM

Assume, for the present, that every simple kernel has a proper value. It follows from this assumption that, if G is a simple surface whose XY-projection is the rectangular interval $[ab;ab]$ which is symmetric, continuous at each of its ordered pairs, and has no proper value, then $G(P) = 0$ for every point P in $[ab;ab]$.

Theorems.   Suppose K is a simple kernel.
1. Suppose the finite orthonormal subset $\phi_1 \ldots \phi_n$ of $M[a,b]$ is a complete orthonormal set of proper functions of K, and ϕ_p belongs to the proper value λ_p of K, $(p = 1 \ldots n)$. If G is the simple surface with XY-projection $[ab;ab]$, defined for each point (x,y) in $[ab;ab]$ by

$$G(x,y) = K(x,y) - \sum_{p=1}^{n} \frac{\phi_p(x)\phi_p(y)}{\lambda_p} ,$$

146

then G is continuous and symmetric, and has no proper value, so that $G(x,y) = 0$ for every (x,y) in $[ab;ab]$. That is,

$$K(x,y) = \sum_{p=1}^{n} \frac{\phi_p(x)\phi_p(y)}{\lambda_p} \quad , \quad a \leq \frac{x}{y} \leq b.$$

Moreover, if the simple graph f is expressible in terms of a simple graph h in $M[a,b]$ as

$$f = Kh,$$

then $f(x) = \sum_{p=1}^{n} ((f,\phi_p)) \cdot \phi_p(x), \quad a \leq x \leq b.$

2. Suppose $\{\phi_p\}_{p=1}^{\infty}$ is a complete orthonormal set of proper functions of K, and ϕ_p belongs to the proper value λ_p of K, $p = 1$, $2,3\ldots$. Suppose, moreover, that there exists a simple surface k with XY-projection $[ab;ab]$ such that, if c is a positive number, there exists a positive integer N such that, if n is an integer greater than N and (x,y) in $[ab;ab]$, then

$$\left| k(x,y) - \sum_{p=1}^{n} \frac{\phi_p(x)\phi_p(y)}{\lambda_p} \right| < c.$$

The following statements are true:
  (i) k is continuous and symmetric,
  (ii) if $G = k - K$, then G is continuous and symmetric, and has no proper value, so that $G(x,y) = 0$ for every (x,y) in $[ab;ab]$; i.e.,

$$k = K.$$

Note. We express this last result briefly as,

$$K(x,y) = \sum_{p=1}^{\infty} \frac{\phi_p(x)\phi_p(y)}{\lambda_p} \quad , \quad \text{uniformly on } [ab;ab].$$

Analogous abbreviations will be used in the sequel.
  Moreover, if the simple graph f is expressible in terms of a simple graph h in $M[a,b]$ as $f = Kh$, then

$$f = \sum_{p=1}^{\infty} ((f,\phi_p)) \cdot \phi_p, \quad \text{uniformly on } [a,b].$$

Note. The last statement means, if c is a positive number, there exists a positive integer N such that, if n is an integer greater than N and x is in $[a,b]$,

$$\left| f(x) - \sum_{p=1}^{n} (\!(f, \phi_p)\!) \cdot \phi_p(x) \right| < c.$$

AN IMPORTANT SPECIAL CASE

We have seen that the set $\phi_p = \sqrt{2} \cdot S[\pi p I]$, $p = 1,2,3 \ldots$, is a complete orthonormal set of proper functions of the simple kernel K defined by

$$K(x,y) = \begin{cases} x(1-y), & \text{if } 0 \le x \le y \le 1, \\ y(1-x), & \text{if } 0 \le y \le x \le 1. \end{cases}$$

The hypothesis of No. 2 of the preceding section is satisfied, and, consequently,

(i)
$$K(x,y) = \sum_{p=1}^{\infty} \frac{2 \cdot S(\pi p x) S(\pi p y)}{\pi^2 p^2},$$

uniformly for $0 \le \dfrac{x}{y} \le 1$.

The simple graph f is expressible in terms of an h of $M[0,1]$ only if f'' has X-projection $[0,1]$, f'' is continuous, and $f(0) = 0$, $f(1) = 0$. For any such f,

(ii)
$$f(x) = \sum_{p=1}^{\infty} 2 \cdot \left\{ \int_0^1 f \cdot S[\pi p I] \right\} \cdot S(\pi p x),$$

uniformly for $0 \le x \le 1$.

There are interesting special cases. For instance, if $y = x$, (i) becomes

(iii)
$$x(1-x) = \sum_{p=1}^{\infty} \frac{2S^2(\pi p x)}{\pi^2 p^2}.$$

Exercises

i. The slope, $D_x \{I(1-I)\}$, is $1 - 2x$. It is obviously *not* true that

$$1 - 2x = \sum_{p=1}^{\infty} D_x \left\{ \frac{2S^2[p\pi I]}{\pi^2 p^2} \right\} = 2 \sum_{p=1}^{\infty} \frac{S(2\pi p x)}{\pi p},$$

if $x = 0$ or if $x = 1$. Prove that this formula *is* true *uniformly* for $u \leq x \leq v$ for any interval $[u,v]$ such that $0 < u < v < 1$.

ii. Show that $\dfrac{\pi^2}{8} = \displaystyle\sum_{p = 1}^{\infty} \left\{\dfrac{1}{2p - 1}\right\}^2$.

iii. Investigate the simple graphs F_k defined, for every number x and positive integer k, by

$$F_1(x) = \begin{cases} 0, & \text{if } x = 0, \\ x - (1/2), & \text{if } 0 < x < 1, \\ 0, & \text{if } x = 1, \end{cases} \quad F_k(x) = F_k(x + 1); \quad \int_0^1 F_k = 0;$$

$$F_{k + 1}(x) = F_{k + 1}(0) + \int_0^x F_k, \quad \text{if } 0 \leq x \leq 1.$$

SECOND EXPANSION THEOREM

Definition. The statement that the simple kernel K is *positive definite* means that if h is in $M[a,b]$, then

$$\int_a^b \int_a^b K(x,y)h(x)h(y)dx\,dy \geq 0.$$

Theorem. If the simple kernel K is positive definite, then every proper value of K is positive.

Suppose $\phi_1 \ldots \phi_n$ is an orthonormal subset of $M[a,b]$ and each of $\lambda_1 \ldots \lambda_n$ is a number distinct from 0, and consider the simple kernel (studied previously),

$$K(x,y) = \sum_{p = 1}^{n} \frac{\phi_p(x)\phi_p(y)}{\lambda_p} .$$

Is there a simple formula, involving an integral, relating K to the following simple kernel:

$$K^{(2)}(x,y) = \sum_{p = 1}^{n} \frac{\phi_p(x)\phi_p(y)}{\lambda_p^2} \quad ?$$

Certainly, every proper value of $K^{(2)}$ is positive.

Definition. If K is a simple kernel and n a positive integer, $K^{(n)}$ (read K *upper n*) is defined, for each point (x,y) in $[ab;ab]$, by

$$K^{(1)} = K,$$

$$K^{(n+1)}(x,y) = \int_a^b K^{(n)}[x,I] \cdot K[I,y].$$

Theorems. Suppose K is a simple kernel.

1. If each of m and n is a positive integer,

$$K^{(m+n)}(x,y) = \int_a^b K^{(m)}[x,I] \cdot K^{(n)}[I,y].$$

2. If n is a positive integer, then $K^{(2n)}$ is a positive definite simple kernel.

3. If the simple kernel K has the proper value λ, then $K^{(2)}$ has the proper value λ^2. If $K^{(2)}$ has the proper value λ^2, then K has the proper value λ or K has the proper value $-\lambda$.

4. Any complete orthonormal set of proper functions of K is a complete orthonormal set of proper functions of $K^{(2)}$ (hence, of $K^{(4)}$, $K^{(8)}$ ...).

Lemma. If each of $a_1 \ldots a_n$ and $b_1 \ldots b_n$ is a number n-tuple, then

$$\left\{ \sum_{p=1}^n a_p b_p \right\}^2 \leq \left\{ \sum_{p=1}^n a_p^2 \right\} \left\{ \sum_{p=1}^n b_p^2 \right\}.$$

Theorems. Suppose K is a simple kernel and $\{\phi_p\}_{p=1}^\infty$ is a complete orthonormal set of proper functions of K and ϕ_p belongs to the proper value λ_p of K, $p = 1,2,3 \ldots$.

1. There exists a number d^2 such that, if t is in $[a,b]$,

$$\sum_{p=1}^n \left[\frac{\phi_p|(t)}{\lambda_p} \right]^2 \leq d^2, \quad n = 1,2,3 \ldots .$$

2. There exists a simple surface k with XY-projection $[ab;ab]$ such that, if x is in $[a,b]$,

$$k(x,y) = \sum_{p=1}^\infty \frac{\phi_p(x)\phi_p(y)}{\lambda_p^2},$$

uniformly for $a \leq y \leq b$.

3.
$$K^{(4)}(x,y) = \sum_{p=1}^{\infty} \frac{\phi_p(x)\phi_p(y)}{\lambda_p^4}$$

uniformly for $a \le \dfrac{x}{y} \le b$.

4. $k = K^{(2)}$.

5. If h is in $M[a,b]$ and $\int_a^b \phi_p h = 0$, *i.e.*, $(\!(\phi_p, h)\!) = 0$, for every positive integer p, then, if x is in $[a,b]$

$$\int_a^b K^{(4)}[x,I]h = 0,$$

$$\int_a^b K^{(2)}[x,I]h = 0,$$

$$\int_a^b K[x,I]h = 0.$$

6. If the simple graph f can be represented in terms of a g in $M[a,b]$ by the formula $f = Kg$, then

$$f = \sum_{p=1}^{\infty} (\!(f,\phi_p)\!) \cdot \phi_p, \quad \text{uniformly on } [a,b].$$

7. If g is in $M[a,b]$,

$$\int_a^b \int_a^b K(x,y)g(x)g(y)\,dx\,dy = \sum_{p=1}^{\infty} \frac{(\!(g,\phi_p)\!)^2}{\lambda_p}.$$

8. If every proper value of K is positive, then K is positive definite. (By this and an earlier result, K is positive definite *only if* each of its proper values is positive.)

9. If K has a positive proper value and λ_1 is the smallest positive proper value of K then, if g is in $M[a,b]$ and $\|g\| = 1$,

$$\int_a^b \int_a^b K(x,y)g(x)g(y)dxdy \le \frac{1}{\lambda_1},$$

with equality in case $g = \phi_1$.

THIRD EXPANSION THEOREM

Lemma. Suppose, for each positive integer n, f_n belongs to $M[a,b]$ and, if x is in $[a,b]$, $f_n(x) \le f_{n+1}(x)$. Suppose f belongs to $M[a,b]$ and, if x is in $[a,b]$ and c is a positive number, there is a number N such that, if $n > N$, $0 \leq f(x) - f_n(x) < c$. Then, if c is a positive number, there exists a number N such that, if x is in $[a,b]$ and $n > N$, $0 \leq f(x) - f_n(x) < c$.

Theorems. Suppose K is a positive definite simple kernel with the complete orthonormal set of proper functions $\{\phi_p\}_{p=1}^{\infty}$ and suppose that, for each positive integer p, ϕ_p belongs to the proper value λ_p of K.

1. If, for each positive integer n, K_n is the simple surface defined, for each (x,y) in $[ab;ab]$, by

$$K_n(x,y) = K(x,y) - \sum_{p=1}^{n} \frac{\phi_p(x)\phi_p(y)}{\lambda_p} \, ,$$

then K_n is a positive definite simple kernel.

2. If x is in $[a,b]$ and n is a positive integer, $K_n(x,x) \geq 0$; *i.e.*,

$$\sum_{p=1}^{n} \frac{\phi_p^2(x)}{\lambda_p} \leq K(x,x).$$

3. There exists a simple surface k with XY-projection $[ab;ab]$ such that, if x is in $[a,b]$,

$$k(x,y) = \sum_{p=1}^{\infty} \frac{\phi_p(x)\phi_p(y)}{\lambda_p} \, ,$$

uniformly for $a \leq y \leq b$.

4. The simple graph g defined, for each x in $[a,b]$, by $g(x) = k(x,x)$ is continuous.

5.
$$g(x) = \sum_{p=1}^{\infty} \frac{\phi_p^2(x)}{\lambda_p} \, , \quad \text{uniformly on } [a,b].$$

6.
$$K(x,y) = \sum_{p=1}^{\infty} \frac{\phi_p(x)\phi_p(y)}{\lambda_p} \, , \quad \text{uniformly on } [ab;ab].$$

Corollary. If K is a simple kernel, then

$$K^{(2)}(x,y) = \sum_{p=1}^{\infty} \frac{\phi_p(x)\phi_p(y)}{\lambda_p^2} \, , \quad \textit{uniformly on } [ab;ab].$$

152

EVERY SIMPLE KERNEL HAS A PROPER VALUE

A study of the simple kernel K, defined in terms of the orthonormal subset $\phi_1 \ldots \phi_n$ of $M[a,b]$ and the number n-tuple $\lambda_1 \ldots \lambda_n$ by

$$K(x,y) = \sum_{p=1}^{n} \frac{\phi_p(x)\phi_p(y)}{\lambda_p} \,,$$

furnishes a clue to a proof that every simple kernel has a proper value.

If m is a positive integer,

$$K^{(m)}(x,y) = \sum_{p=1}^{n} \frac{\phi_p(x)\phi_p(y)}{\lambda_p^m} \,,$$

and, consequently,

$$\int_a^b K^{(m)}[I,I] = \sum_{p=1}^{n} \left(\frac{1}{\lambda_p}\right)^m \,.$$

If λ^2 denotes the largest number r such that $r \leq (\lambda_p)^2$, $p = 1 \ldots n$, and $u_m = \sum_{p=1}^{n} \left(\frac{1}{\lambda_p}\right)^{2m}$, $m = 1,2,3 \ldots$, then it is easy to see that the number sequence $\left\{\dfrac{u_m}{u_{m+1}}\right\}_{m=1}^{\infty}$ converges to the sequential limit λ^2. This suggests that, for any simple kernel K, if

$$u_m = \int_a^b K^{(2m)}[I,I], \quad m = 1,2,3 \ldots ,$$

then the number sequence $\left(\dfrac{u_m}{u_{m+1}}\right)_{m=1}^{\infty}$ may be proved to converge to λ^2, that λ^2 is a proper value of $K^{(2)}$, and that, therefore, K has the proper value λ or else the proper value $-\lambda$.

ORTHOGONAL POLYNOMIALS

We return to the transformation Z of an earlier section defined by

$$Zf = -\{(1 - I^2)f'\}',$$

for f with X-projection the segment Δ with ends -1 and 1, having a continuous second derivative f'' with X-projection Δ.

G_1 denotes the set of all such simple graphs f such that f', and therefore f, is bounded on Δ.

Definition. The statement that λ is a proper value of the transformation Z, and ϕ a proper function of Z belonging to λ, means that λ is a number and ϕ an element of G_1, distinct from $\underline{0}$, such that

$$Z\phi = \lambda \cdot \phi .$$

Examples

i. 0 is a proper value of Z and $\underline{1}$ (restricted to Δ) a proper function of Z belonging to the proper value 0.

ii. 2 is a proper value of Z and I (restricted to Δ) a proper function of Z belonging to the proper value 2.

Note. We restrict all simple graphs in this discussion to the segment Δ.

If f is a simple graph, $f^{(0)}$, the "zero-th derivative of f" denotes f itself; $f^{(1)} = f'$, $f^{(2)} = f''$, and, if n is a positive integer, $f^{(n+1)} = \{f^{(n)}\}'$; $f^{(n)}$ is called the n-th derivative of f.

Lemma. If n is a positive integer,

$$(uv)^{(n)} = u^{(n)}v^{(0)} + \frac{n}{1}u^{(n-1)}v^{(1)} + \frac{n(n-1)}{1\cdot 2}u^{(n-2)}v^{(2)} + \ldots$$

$$+ \frac{n(n-1)\ldots(n-r+1)}{1\cdot 2\cdot \ldots \cdot r}u^{(n-r)}v^{(r)} + \ldots + u^{(0)}v^{(n)} ,$$

for any simple graph u and simple graph v having the derivatives indicated.

If n is a positive integer, the statement that Q_n is a polynomial of degree n means that Q_n is a simple graph $a_0 I^n + a_1 I^{n-1} + \ldots + a_n$ where each of $a_0 \ldots a_n$ is a number and $a_0 \neq 0$.

Theorems. Suppose λ is a number, n a positive integer, and Q_n a polynomial of degree n such that $ZQ_n = \lambda \cdot Q_n$.

1. If k is a positive integer,

$$\{(1 - I^2)^k Q_n^{(k)}\}' = -\{\lambda - (k-1)k\}(1 - I^2)^{k-1}Q_n^{(k-1)} .$$

2. $\lambda = n(n+1)$.

3. $\{(1 - I^2)^n Q_n^{(n)}\}^{(n)} =$

$$(-1)^n \{\lambda - (n-1)n\}\{\lambda - (n-2)(n-1)\}\ldots\{\lambda - 1\cdot 2\}\cdot \lambda \cdot Q_n ,$$

so that, for some number k_n distinct from 0,

$$Q_n = k_n \cdot \{(1 - I^2)^n\}^{(n)} .$$

Examples. $Q_0 = k_0$; $Q_1 = k_1 \cdot (-2I)$; $Q_2 = k_2 \cdot \{-4(1 - 3I^2)\}$. We determine $k_0, k_1 \ldots$ so that $Q_n(1) = 1$. Then, $k_0 = 1$, $k_1 = -(1/2)$, $k_2 = (1/8)$. We denote the polynomial Q_n, with k_n so determined, by P_n. Then,

$$P_0 = \underline{1}, \qquad P_1 = I, \qquad P_2 = \frac{1}{2}(3I^2 - 1) .$$

Theorems. Suppose n is a positive integer and

$$Q_n = \{(1 - I^2)^n\}^{(n)} .$$

1. $Q_n = (1 - I^2)Q'_{n-1} - 2nIQ_{n-1} - n(n-1)h$, where $h(x) = \int_{-1}^{x} Q_{n-1}$.

2. If $ZQ_{n-1} = (n-1)nQ_{n-1}$, then

$$Q'_n = -2nIQ'_{n-1} - 2n^2Q_{n-1}, \quad Q_n = 2(1 - I^2)Q'_{n-1} - 2nIQ_{n-1},$$

$$\text{and} \quad ZQ_n = n(n+1)Q_n .$$

3. $Q_n(1) = (-1)^n 2^n \cdot 1 \cdot 2 \cdot \ldots \cdot n$.

4. $P_0 = \underline{1}$ and $P_n = \dfrac{1}{2^n \cdot 1 \cdot 2 \cdot \ldots \cdot n} \cdot \{(I^2 - 1)^n\}^{(n)}$.

Inasmuch as $ZP_n = n(n+1)P_n$, $n = 0,1,2 \ldots$, then $n(n+1)$ is a proper value of Z ($n = 0,1,2 \ldots$) and P_n a proper function of Z belonging to the proper value $n(n+1)$ of Z.

Theorem. If ϕ is a proper function of Z belonging to the proper value $n(n+1)$, where n is a nonnegative integer, then there exists a number k distinct from 0 such that $\phi = k \cdot P_n$. If λ is a number distinct from $n(n+1)$, $n = 0,1,2 \ldots$, then λ is not a proper value of Z.

Theorem. If each of m and n is a nonnegative integer,

$$\int_{-1}^{1} P_m P_n = \begin{cases} 0, & \text{if } m \neq n, \\ \dfrac{2}{2n+1}, & \text{if } m = n. \end{cases}$$

More about Linear Spaces

The space in which *point* means number sequence, with addition of the number sequence a and the number sequence b defined by

$$(a + b)_p = a_p + b_p, \quad p = 1, 2, 3 \ldots ,$$

and multiplication of a by the number k defined by

$$(k \cdot a)_p = ka_p, \quad p = 1, 2, 3 \ldots ,$$

is a linear space. We denote this linear space of *all* number sequences by W. If a is a point of W for which there is a number k_1 such that

$$\sum_{p=1}^{n} a_p^2 \leq k_1, \quad n = 1, 2, 3 \ldots ,$$

and b is a point of W for which there is a number k_2 such that

$$\sum_{p=1}^{n} b_p^2 \leq k_2, \quad n = 1, 2, 3 \ldots ,$$

then

$$\sum_{p=1}^{n} (a_p + b_p)^2 = \sum_{p=1}^{n} a_p^2 + \sum_{p=1}^{n} b_p^2 + 2 \sum_{p=1}^{n} a_p b_p$$

$$\leq k_1 + k_2 + 2 \left\{ \sum_{p=1}^{n} a_p^2 \cdot \sum_{p=1}^{n} b_p^2 \right\}^{1/2} \leq (k_1^{1/2} + k_2^{1/2})^2 ,$$

so that $a + b$ has the same property. Also, if k is a number, $\sum_{p=1}^{n}(ka)_p^2 = k^2\sum_{p=1}^{n}a_p^2 \le k^2 k_1$, so that $k \cdot a$ has the same property.

Definition. $\mathcal{H}$ denotes the linear space in which *point* means number sequence a such that, for some number k, $\sum_{p=1}^{n}a_p^2 \le k$, for every positive integer n, with addition and multiplication by a number defined as in the linear space W and with the inner product defined for every point a and b by

$$(\!(a,b)\!) = \sum_{p=1}^{\infty} a_p b_p .$$

(That is, if ϵ is a positive number, there exists a number m such that $|(\!(a,b)\!) - \sum_{p=1}^{n} a_p b_p| < \epsilon$ if $n > m$.)

Note. We are interested in the linear space $\mathcal{H}$ primarily because we have seen in the preceding chapter that certain simple graphs f have associated with them points a of $\mathcal{H}$ defined by $a_p = (\!(f,\phi_p)\!)$, $p = 1, 2, 3 \ldots$. (See the second expansion theorem.)

PROPERTIES OF THE SPACE $\mathcal{H}$

1. If n is a positive integer, E_n denotes the linear space in which *point* means ordered number n-tuple $(a_1 \ldots a_n)$ with addition and multiplication by a number k defined by

$$(a_1 \ldots a_n) + (b_1 \ldots b_n) = (a_1 + b_1 \ldots a_n + b_n)$$

and

$$k \cdot (a_1 \ldots a_n) = (ka_1 \ldots ka_n);$$

and with inner product $(\!(a,b)\!) = a_1 b_1 + \ldots + a_n b_n$. E_n is described as *isometric with* the subspace $\mathcal{H}^{(n)}$ of all points a of $\mathcal{H}$ such that $a_p = 0$ if $p > n$. This means that there exists a reversible transformation F from E_n to $\mathcal{H}^{(n)}$ which is *linear*, i.e., if a is in E_n, b in E_n, and k a number, then $F(a + b) = F(a) + F(b)$ and $F(k \cdot a) = k \cdot F(a)$; and *distance preserving*, i.e., the distance from the point a of E_n to the point b of E_n is the distance from the point $F(a)$ of $\mathcal{H}^{(n)}$ to the point $F(b)$ of $\mathcal{H}^{(n)}$. In fact, such a transformation is given by

$$F(a_1 \ldots a_n) = (a_1 \ldots a_n,0,0 \ldots) .$$

2. Suppose G is an infinite point set in E_n which is *bounded*; *i.e.*, there is a number r such that, if x is in G, then $\|x\| \le r$. Then there is a point a of G, called a *limit point* of G, such that, if r is a positive number, there exists an infinite subset G_1 of G such that, if x is in G_1, $\|x - a\| < r$. The space $\mathcal{H}$ does not have this property. There exists an infinite point set G in $\mathcal{H}$ such that, if x is in G, $\|x\| = 1$, and, if x and y are points of G, $\|x - y\| > 1$.

3. There exists in $\mathcal{H}$ a point sequence $\{a^{(p)}\}_{p=1}^{\infty}$; *i.e.*, if p is a positive integer, $a^{(p)}$ is a point of $\mathcal{H}$, such that, if x is a point of $\mathcal{H}$ and r a positive number, there is a positive integer p such that $\|x - a^{(p)}\| < r$.

4. The statement that the point sequence $\{b^{(p)}\}_{p=1}^{\infty}$ in $\mathcal{H}$ is a *closing sequence*, means that, if ϵ is a positive number, there exists a number k such that $\|b^{(m)} - b^{(n)}\| < \epsilon$ if $m > k$ and $n > k$. Every closing point sequence in $\mathcal{H}$ converges to a point of $\mathcal{H}$. That is, if $\{b^{(p)}\}_{p=1}^{\infty}$ is a closing point sequence in $\mathcal{H}$, there exists a point a in $\mathcal{H}$ such that, if ϵ is a positive number, there exists a number m such that $\|a - b^{(n)}\| < \epsilon$ if $n > m$.

5. There exists a point sequence $\{\phi^{(p)}\}_{p=1}^{\infty}$ in $\mathcal{H}$ with the following properties:

(i)
$$\langle\langle \phi^{(p)}, \phi^{(q)} \rangle\rangle = \begin{cases} 0, & \text{if } p \ne q, \\ 1, & \text{if } p = q; \end{cases}$$

and

(ii) if x is a point of $\mathcal{H}$ and ϵ a positive number, there exists a number m such that $\|x - \sum_{p=1}^{n} \langle\langle \phi^{(p)}, x \rangle\rangle \cdot \phi^{(p)}\| < \epsilon$ if $n > m$.

6. Any inner product space having the properties of $\mathcal{H}$ indicated in Numbers 2, 3, and 4 is isometric with $\mathcal{H}$.

Further discussion is undesirable inasmuch as we do not want to spoil these good problems for the reader.

LINEAR TRANSFORMATIONS IN $\mathcal{H}$

Suppose T is a transformation from $\mathcal{H}$ to a number set.

i. The statement that T is linear means that if each of a and b is a point of $\mathcal{H}$ and k a number, then

$$T(a + b) = Ta + Tb, \text{ and } T(k \cdot a) = k \, Ta.$$

ii. The statement that T is continuous means that, if a is a point of H and ϵ a positive number, there exists a positive number δ such that, if x is a point of $\mathcal{H}$ and $\| x - a \| < \delta$, then $| Tx - Ta | < \epsilon$.

iii. The statement that T is bounded means there exists a number k such that, if x is a point of $\mathcal{H}$, then $| Tx | \le k \| x \|$.

Theorem. Suppose T is a linear transformation from $\mathcal{H}$ to a number set. The following two statements are equivalent:

(i) T is continuous

and

(ii) T is bounded.

Example. If a is a point of $\mathcal{H}$ and T the transformation from $\mathcal{H}$ to a number set defined, for each x in $\mathcal{H}$, by

$$Tx = (\!(a,x)\!),$$

then T is linear and bounded, and the least number k such that $| Tx | \le k \| x \|$ for every x in $\mathcal{H}$ is the number $\| a \|$.

Theorem. If T is a bounded linear transformation from $\mathcal{H}$ to a number set, then there exists a point a of $\mathcal{H}$ such that, if x is a point of $\mathcal{H}$, $Tx = (\!(a,x)\!)$.

Problem. Show that there is a linear space isometric with $\mathcal{H}$ in which point means bounded linear transformation from $\mathcal{H}$ to a number set.

1. Suppose F is a transformation from the set of ordered pairs x,y, each member of which is a point of $\mathcal{H}$, to a number set.

i. The statement that F is *bilinear* means that, if each of x,y, and z is a point of $\mathcal{H}$ and k a number,

$$F(x + y, z) = F(x, z) + F(y, z),$$
$$F(x, y + z) = F(x, y) + F(x, z),$$

and

$$F(k \cdot x, y) = F(x, k \cdot y) = kF(x, y).$$

ii. The statement that F is *bounded* means that there exists a number k such that, if each of x and y is a point of $\mathcal{H}$,

$$| F(x,y) | \le k \| x \| \, \| y \|.$$

2. Suppose f is a transformation from the set of points of $\mathcal{H}$ to a point set in $\mathcal{H}$.

i. The statement that f is *linear* means that, if each of x and y is a point of $\mathcal{H}$ and k a number, then

$$f(x + y) = fx + fy \text{ and } f(k \cdot x) = k \cdot fx.$$

ii. The statement that f is *bounded* means that there exists a number k such that, if x is a point of $\mathcal{H}$,

$$\| fx \| \le k \| x \|.$$

Theorems. Suppose F is a transformation from the ordered pairs x, y, with first member a point of $\mathcal{H}$ and second member a point of $\mathcal{H}$, to a number set.

1. If f is a bounded linear transformation from $\mathcal{H}$ to a point set in $\mathcal{H}$ and, if x is a point of $\mathcal{H}$ and y a point of $\mathcal{H}$, $F(x,y) = (\!(fx,y)\!)$, then F is bilinear and bounded.

2. If F is bilinear and bounded, there exists only one bounded linear transformation f from $\mathcal{H}$ to a point set in $\mathcal{H}$ and only one bounded linear transformation $f*$ from $\mathcal{H}$ to a point set in $\mathcal{H}$ such that, if x is a point of $\mathcal{H}$ and y a point of $\mathcal{H}$,

$$F(x,y) = (\!(fx,y)\!) \text{ and } F(x,y) = (\!(x,f*y)\!).$$

The bounded linear transformations f and $f*$ from $\mathcal{H}$ to point sets in $\mathcal{H}$ are called *adjoints* of one another.

Definition. The statement that f is a *matrix* means that f is a transformation from the set of ordered positive integer pairs to a number set. If f is a matrix and p,q an ordered positive pair, each member of which is a positive integer, we denote $f(p,q)$ by f_{pq}. The statement that the matrix f is *bounded* means that there exists a number k such that, if n is a positive integer, $x_1 \ldots x_n$ a number n-tuple, and $y_1 \ldots y_n$ a number n-tuple, then,

$$\left| \sum_{p,q=1}^{n} x_p f_{pq} y_q \right| \le k \left\{ \sum_{p=1}^{n} x_p^2 \cdot \sum_{q=1}^{n} y_q^2 \right\}^{1/2}.$$

Theorem. The set of bounded matrices may be identified with the set of bounded linear transformations from $\mathcal{H}$ to point sets in $\mathcal{H}$ so that, if f is such a transformation, if x is the point $\{x_p\}_{p=1}^{\infty}$ of $\mathcal{H}$, if $fx = y = \{y_p\}_{p=1}^{\infty}$, and if the same letter f is used to denote the bounded matrix identified with this transformation, then

$$y_p = \sum_{q=1}^{\infty} f_{pq} x_q, \quad p = 1, 2, 3 \ldots.$$

Note. The adjoint $f*$ of f is defined by

$$f_{pq}^* = f_{qp}.$$

THE SPACE $C_0[a,b]$

This is the linear space in which point means simple graph f with the following properties: f has X-projection the interval $[a,b]$, f is continuous, $f(a) = 0$, and the norm of f is defined by

$$\|f\|_0 = \begin{bmatrix} \text{The least number } k \text{ such that} \\ |f(x)| \le k \text{ for every } x \text{ in } [a,b] \end{bmatrix}.$$

Suppose $\{t_p\}_{p=1}^{\infty}$ is a number sequence such that

i. $a < t_p \le b$, $p = 1, 2, 3 \ldots ,$

ii. $t_p \neq t_q$, if $p \neq q$,

and

iii. if s is a subinterval of $[a,b]$, there exists a positive integer p such that t_p is in s.

For each positive integer p, θ_p denotes the simple graph in $C_0[a,b]$ defined as follows:

$$\theta_p(x) = \begin{cases} x, & \text{if } a \le x \le t_p, \\ t_p, & \text{if } t_p \le x \le b. \end{cases}$$

Theorems

1. If n is a positive integer and $k_1 \ldots k_n$ a number n-tuple such that $k_1 \cdot \theta_1 + \ldots + k_n \cdot \theta_n = 0$, then $k_1 = \ldots = k_n = 0$.

2. If f is a point of $C_0[a,b]$ and ϵ a positive number, there exists a positive integer n and a number n-tuple $k_1 \ldots k_n$ such that

$$\left\| f - \sum_{p=1}^{n} k_p \cdot \theta_p \right\|_0 < \epsilon .$$

THE SPACE $BV_0[a,b]$

We first state the following theorem, which includes some ideas previously introduced.

Theorem. Suppose f is a simple graph with X-projection the interval $[a,b]$ which is of bounded variation on $[a,b]$.

1. If c is a number between a and b, then f is of bounded variation on $[a,c]$ and on $[c,b]$ and the total variation of f on $[a,b]$ is the sum of the total variation of f on $[a,c]$ plus the total variation of f on $[c,b]$:

$$V_a^b f = V_a^c f + V_c^b f.$$

2. If ϕ_1 denotes the simple graph with X-projection $[a,b]$ such that

$$\phi_1(x) = \begin{cases} 0, & \text{if } x = a, \\ V_a^x f & \text{if } a < x \le b, \end{cases}$$

then,

    (i) ϕ_1 is nondecreasing on $[a,b]$,

    (ii) $f + \phi_1$ is nondecreasing on $[a,b]$,

and

    (iii) if $f + \phi_1$ is denoted by ϕ_2, we see that $f = \phi_2 - \phi_1$, the difference of two nondecreasing simple graphs.

3. f has "property (Q)" at each of its points.

Note. In the notation in the first of the "two questions" on page 90, if the abscissa of P is x, we denote P_L by $(x, f(x-))$ in case $a < x \le b$, and P_R by $(x, f(x+))$ in case $a \le x < b$.

Definition. $BV_0[a,b]$ is the linear space in which point means simple graph f with the following properties: f has X-projection $[a,b]$, $f(a) = 0$, f is of bounded variation on $[a,b]$, the norm of f is

$$\|f\|_{bv} = V_a^b f;$$

and, if $a \le x < b$,

$$f(x) = f(x+).$$

Theorem. If f is in $BV_0[a,b]$, denote by $\|f\|_0$ (as in the space $C_0[a,b]$) the least number k such that $|f(x)| \le k$ for every x in $[a,b]$. If f is in $BV_0[a,b]$, then

$$\|f\|_0 \le \|f\|_{bv}.$$

THE SPACE $C_m[a,b]$

The points of this space are the same as the points of $C_0[a,b]$, but there is a different norm. The letter m denotes a simple graph with X-projection $[a,b]$ which is *increasing*; i.e., if $a \le x < y \le b$, then $m(x) < m(y)$, $m(a) = 0$, and, if $a \le x < b$, $m(x) = m(x+)$. If f is in $C_m[a,b]$ and g in $C_m[a,b]$, the inner product of f and g is

$$((f,g))_m = \int_a^b fg \, dm.$$

Thus, $C_m[a,b]$ is an inner product space with norm,

$$\|f\|_m = \left\{ \int_a^b f^2 \, dm \right\}^{1/2}.$$

Theorem. Suppose θ_1, θ_2, $\theta_3, \ldots$ is the sequence of simple graphs in $C_0[a,b]$ defined previously in terms of the number sequence $\{t_p\}_{p=1}^{\infty}$,

$$\phi_1 = \frac{\theta_1}{\|\theta_1\|_m}$$

and, if p is a positive integer,

$$\phi_{p+1} = \frac{\theta_{p+1} - \sum_{q=1}^{p} (\!(\theta_{p+1}, \phi_q)\!)_m \cdot \phi_q}{\left\| \theta_{p+1} - \sum_{q=1}^{p} (\!(\theta_{p+1}, \phi_q)\!)_m \cdot \phi_q \right\|_m}.$$

Then the following statements are true.

(i) $(\!(\phi_i, \phi_j)\!)_m$ is 0 if $i \neq j$, and 1 if $i = j$.

(ii) If n is a positive integer, there exists a number n-tuple $k_1 \ldots k_n$ such that $\theta_n = k_1 \cdot \phi_1 + \ldots + k_n \cdot \phi_n$ and a number n-tuple $h_1 \ldots h_n$ such that $\phi_n = h_1 \cdot \theta_1 + \ldots + h_n \cdot \theta_n$.

(iii) If f is in $C_0[a,b]$ and ϵ is a positive number, there exists a number n-tuple $k_1 \ldots k_n$, for some positive integer n, such that $\left\| f - \sum_{p=1}^{n} k_p \cdot \phi_p \right\|_0 < \epsilon$.

(iv) If f is in $C_m[a,b]$ and ϵ is a positive number, there exists a number k such that $\left\| f - \sum_{p=1}^{n} (\!(f, \phi_p)\!)_m \cdot \phi_p \right\|_m < \epsilon$ if $n > k$.

Definition. *Any* sequence ϕ_1, ϕ_2, $\phi_3 \ldots$ of points of $C_m[a,b]$ having properties (i), (iii), and, therefore, (iv), of the preceding theorem is called a *uniformly complete orthonormal set in* $C_m[a,b]$.

Note. The "second expansion theorem" of the preceding chapter furnishes another example of a uniformly complete orthonormal set in an inner product space of simple graphs.

Lemma. Suppose each of f, g, and m is a simple graph with X-projection the interval $[a,b]$, f is continuous, g is continuous, and m nondecreasing. If h is the simple graph with X-projection $[a,b]$ defined by $h(x) = \int_a^x g \, dm$, $a \leq x \leq b$, then

$$\int_a^b f \, dh = \int_a^b fg \, dm.$$

Problem. Suppose $\{\phi_p\}_{p=1}^{\infty}$ is a uniformly complete orthonormal set in $C_m[a,b]$ and x is a point of $\mathcal{H}$. Determine a simple graph X in $BV_0[a,b]$ such that, for every positive integer p,

$$x_p = \int_a^b \phi_p \, dX.$$

Suggestion. Try to "guess" the solution. We urge the reader to try to settle this problem before looking ahead.

It turns out that there is *only one* such solution X. Thus, there exists a reversible and linear transformation from $\mathcal{H}$ to a point set in $BV_0[a,b]$. Moreover, there is an inner product space $H^m[a,b]$, the set of whose points is this point set in $BV_0[a,b]$, which is *isometric* with $\mathcal{H}$.

The outline given in this chapter is designed to lead the reader to establish this result.

Theorems. Suppose x is a point of $\mathcal{H}$ and, if n is a positive integer, X_n is the simple graph with X-projection $[a,b]$ defined, for each s in $[a,b]$, by

$$X_n(s) = \sum_{p=1}^{n} x_p \int_a^s \phi_p \, dm.$$

1. X_n is a point in $BV_0[a,b]$.
2. If q is a positive integer and $n \ge q$,

$$x_q = \int_a^b \phi_q \, dX_n.$$

3. The point sequence in $BV_0[a,b]$, $\{X_n\}_{n=1}^{\infty}$, is a closing sequence in $BV_0[a,b]$; *i.e.*, if ϵ is a positive number, there exists a number k such that $\|X_m - X_n\|_{bv} < \epsilon$, if $m > k$ and $n > k$. Hence, $\|X_m - X_n\|_0 < \epsilon$, if $m > k$ and $n > k$, so that there exists a simple graph X with X-projection $[a,b]$ such that

$$X(s) = \sum_{p=1}^{\infty} x_p \int_a^s \phi_p \, dm, \text{ uniformly for } a \le s \le b.$$

4. X is a point in $BV_0[a,b]$ and, if ϵ is a positive number, there exists a positive integer k such that $\|X - X_n\|_{bv} < \epsilon$ if $n > k$.
5. If q is a positive integer and $n \ge q$,

$$\left| x_q - \int_a^b \phi_q \, dA \right| \le \|\phi_q\|_0 \cdot \|X - X_n\|_{bv},$$

and therefore $x_q = \int_a^b \phi_q \, dA$, $q = 1, 2, 3 \ldots$.

6. If Y is a point of $BV_0[a,b]$ such that $x_q = \int_a^b \phi_q \, dY$, $q = 1, 2, 3 \ldots$, then, if f is in $C_0[a,b]$,

$$\int_a^b f \, d(X - Y) = 0$$

and, as a consequence,

$$Y = X.$$

If X is a point in $BV_0[a,b]$ and

$$x_p = \int_a^b \phi_p \, dX, \quad p = 1, 2, 3 \ldots ,$$

we seek a further condition on X so that $\{x_p\}_{p=1}^{\infty}$ shall be a point x in $\mathcal{H}$; $i.e.$, so that there shall exist a number k for which $\sum_{p=1}^{n} x_p^2 \leq k$, $n = 1, 2, 3 \ldots$.

We write x_p^2 in the form

$$x_p^2 = \int_a^b x_p \phi_p \, dX,$$

so that

$$\sum_{p=1}^{n} x_p^2 = \int_a^b \sum_{p=1}^{n} x_p \phi_p \, dX.$$

By definition of the integral, if ϵ is a positive number, there exists a finite collection D of nonoverlapping intervals filling up $[a,b]$ such that $\int_a^b \sum_{p=1}^{n} x_p \phi_p \, dX < \epsilon + \Sigma \left(\sum_{p=1}^{n} x_p \phi_p (s) \right) \{X(t) - X(r)\}$, summed for all the intervals $[r,t]$ in D with $r \leq s \leq t$. Thus,

$$\sum_{p=1}^{n} x_p^2 < \epsilon + \Sigma \left(\sum_{p=1}^{n} x_p \phi_p (s) \right) Q\{m(t) - m(r)\} \frac{X(t) - X(r)}{Q\{m(t) - m(r)\}}$$

$$< \epsilon + \left\{ \Sigma \left(\sum_{p=1}^{n} x_p \phi_p (s) \right)^2 [m(t) - m(r)] \right\}^{1/2} \left\{ \Sigma \frac{[X(t) - X(r)]^2}{m(t) - m(r)} \right\}^{1/2}.$$

From this it follows that, if there exists a number k such that, for every finite collection D of nonoverlapping intervals filling up $[a,b]$,

$$\sum \frac{[X(t) - X(r)]^2}{m(t) - m(r)} \leq k,$$

the sum being taken for all the intervals $[r,t]$ in D, then

$$\sum_{p=1}^{n} x_p^2 \leq k.$$

We thus have a condition on X which is *sufficient* for x to be a point of $\mathcal{H}$. This condition suggests consideration of an interesting kind of integral.

THE INTEGRAL $\int_a^b \frac{dXdY}{dm}$

Definition. If each of X, Y, and m is a simple graph whose X-projection is the interval $[a,b]$, and if m is *increasing*, then the integral $\int_a^b \frac{dXdY}{dm}$ is a number J such that, if ϵ is a positive number, there exists a finite collection D of nonoverlapping intervals filling up $[a,b]$ such that, if D$'$ is a finite collection of nonoverlapping intervals filling up $[a,b]$, with each end of each interval of D an end of some interval of D$'$, then the sum

$$\sum \frac{\{X(t) - X(r)\} \{Y(t) - Y(r)\}}{m(t) - m(r)},$$

formed for all the intervals $[r,t]$ in D$'$, differs from J by less than ϵ. We shall call this integral *the* H-*integral of* X *and* Y *with respect to* m.

Theorems. Suppose each of X and m is a simple graph with X-projection the interval $[a,b]$ and m is increasing.

1. In order for the H-integral of X and X with respect to m to exist, it is necessary and sufficient that there should exist a number k such that, if D is a finite collection of nonoverlapping intervals filling up $[a,b]$,

$$\sum \frac{\{X(t) - X(r)\}^2}{m(t) - m(r)} \leq k,$$

where the sum is taken for all intervals $[r, t]$ in D. If the condition is satisfied, the least such number k is the integral

$$\int_a^b \frac{(d\mathrm{X})^2}{dm} \, .$$

2. In order for the H-integral of X and X with respect to m to exist, it is necessary and sufficient that there should exist a simple graph h which is nondecreasing on $[a,b]$ such that, if $[r,t]$ is a subinterval of $[a,b]$,

$$\{\mathrm{X}(t) - \mathrm{X}(r)\}^2 \le \{m(t) - m(r)\} \{h(t) - h(r)\} \, .$$

3. If the H-integral of X and X with respect to m exists, then X is continuous at $(t, \mathrm{X}(t))$, $(a \le t \le b)$, in case m is continuous at $(t, m(t))$.

4. If the H-integral of X and X with respect to m exists, then X is of bounded variation on $[a,b]$ and

$$\mathrm{V}_a^b \, \mathrm{X} \le \{m(b) - m(a)\} \cdot \int_a^b \frac{(d\mathrm{X})^2}{dm} \, .$$

5. If the H-integral of X and X with respect to m exists, if the H-integral of Y and Y with respect to m exists and if k is a number, then the H-integral of X and Y with respect to m exists, the H-integral of X + Y and X + Y with respect to m exists, and the H-integral of $k \cdot$ X and $k \cdot$ X with respect to m exists.

Definition. $\mathrm{H}^m [a,b]$ denotes the inner product space in which point means an X in $\mathrm{BV}_0 [a,b]$ such that the H-integral of X and X with respect to m exists (m being the increasing simple graph in $\mathrm{BV}_0 [a,b]$ previously used) with inner product,

$$(\!(\mathrm{X},\mathrm{Y})\!)^m = \int_a^b \frac{d\mathrm{X}d\mathrm{Y}}{dm} \, .$$

Corollary. If X is a point of $\mathrm{H}^m [a,b]$ and $x_p = \int_a^b \phi_p \, d\mathrm{X}$, $p = 1, 2, 3 \ldots$, then $\{x_p\}_{p=1}^\infty$ is a point of $\mathcal{H}$.

Theorem. If x is a point in $\mathcal{H}$ and X *the* point of $\mathrm{BV}_0 [a,b]$ such that $x_p = \int_a^b \phi_p \, d\mathrm{X}$, $p = 1, 2, 3 \ldots$, then X is in $\mathrm{H}^m [a,b]$. Also, if y is a point in $\mathcal{H}$ and Y *the* point of $\mathrm{H}^m [a,b]$ such that $y_p = \int_a^b \phi_p \, d\mathrm{Y}$, $p = 1, 2, 3 \ldots$, then

$$(\!(x, y)\!) = (\!(\mathrm{X},\mathrm{Y})\!)^m \, ;$$

i.e.,

$$\sum_{p=1}^{\infty} \{\int_a^b \phi_p \, dX\}\{\int_a^b \phi_p \, dY\} = \int_a^b \frac{dXdY}{dm} \ .$$

For each increasing m in $BV_0[a,b]$, the inner product space $H^m[a,b]$ is isometric with $\mathcal{H}$.

Mechanical Systems

We consider applications of simple graphs to the analysis of measurable physical things which may vary with time. Each number t is regarded as the measure, in some convenient unit, of the *time* from some specified instant τ, *after* τ if $t > 0$, *before* τ if $t < 0$. Suppose G is a number set each element of which is so regarded. For each t in G, suppose $f(t)$ is the measure (a number) of some physical thing at time t (*i.e.* at the time from τ determined by t). Then, f is a simple graph whose X-projection is G.

Example. Suppose a spherical balloon is being inflated with a gas in such a way that the volume enclosed increases steadily, from a certain instant τ, at the rate of 200 cubic feet per minute. Each number t in a certain interval $[0,a]$ represents the time measured in minutes from τ. Some simple graphs with X-projection $[0,a]$ connected with this situation are

i. the volume V such that, if t is in $[0,a]$, $V(t)$ is the volume, in cubic feet, of gas enclosed by the balloon at time t: $V(t) = 200t + V(0)$;

ii. the surface area s such that, if t is in $[0,a]$, $s(t)$ is the area of the surface of the balloon measured in square feet;

iii. the radius r such that, if t is in $[0,a]$, $r(t)$ is the radius of the balloon measured in feet.

The simple graphs V, s, and r are related to one another by the formulas,

$$V = \frac{4}{3}\pi r^3 \text{ and } s = 4\pi r^2.$$

If f is a simple graph such that, for each t in the number set G, $f(t)$ is the measure of a certain physical thing, then $f'(t)$ is the *rate of change* and $f''(t)$ the *acceleration* of this thing, at time t. In the above example, $V'(t) = 200$, the rate in cubic feet per minute that gas is being forced into the balloon.

Problems

1. In the preceding example, suppose c is the time t such that $r(t) = 10$. Find the rate of change and acceleration of the radius r and of the surface area s of the balloon at time c.

2. Two railroad tracks (straight) intersect at right angles. At a certain instant, one train is 87 miles from the intersection and approaching it at 40 miles per hour and a second train on the other track is 72 miles from the intersection and approaching it at 30 miles per hour. How fast are the trains approaching one another 2 hours later? What is the minimum distance between them during the entire run? Regard each train as a "point" and the speed of each as constant.

3. Suppose each of a, b, and h is a positive number. A man is walking along a straight road at the rate of a feet per second. At a certain instant, he is on a bridge h feet directly above a boat which is going at the rate of b feet per second on a straight river at right angles to the road. How fast are the man and boat separating 2 seconds later? Regard the man as a "point," the boat as a "point" and their speeds as constant.

FALLING BODIES

Problems

1. A body of mass m falls from rest from a place above the earth at a certain instant τ. Suppose s is the simple graph with X-projection the interval $[0,a]$ such that $s(0) = 0$ and, if t is a positive number not greater than a, $s(t)$ is the distance, measured in feet, which the body falls in time t, measured in seconds. Here, a is the least number x such that, if $0 < t < x$, the body is above the earth, so that $s(a)$ is the height of the body above the earth at the instant τ. Assuming that the body is drawn toward the earth by the "force of gravity" and that its motion is retarded by the air resistance, assumed proportional to the velocity, the simple graph s satisfies the equation,

$$ms'' = mg - ks',$$

where each of g and k is a positive number. This is taken for granted. Show that this equation may be written as

$$\left\{ -\frac{m}{k} L\left[g - \frac{k}{m} s' \right] \right\}' = 1$$

(all simple graphs being restricted to $[0,a]$. There is a number c such that

$$-\frac{m}{k} L\left[g - \frac{k}{m} s' \right] = I + c;$$

$$c = -\frac{m}{k} L(g);$$

and

$$s' = \frac{mg}{k} \left\{ 1 - E\left[-\frac{k}{m} I \right] \right\}.$$

Hence show that, if t is in $[0,a]$,

$$s(t) = \frac{mg}{k} \left\{ t - \frac{m}{k} + \frac{m}{k} e^{-\frac{m}{k} t} \right\}.$$

2. Show that, if air resistance is neglected,

$$s(t) = \tfrac{1}{2} g t^2, \quad 0 \leq t \leq a.$$

3. Consider the same problem under the hypothesis that the air resistance is proportional to the *square* of the velocity, so that the equation for s is

$$m s'' = mg - k(s')^2, \quad (k > 0).$$

Denote the number $\dfrac{k}{mg}$ by c^2 and show that this equation may be written as

$$\frac{s''}{2} \left\{ \frac{1}{1 - cs'} + \frac{1}{1 + cs'} \right\} = g$$

or

$$\left\{ \frac{1}{2c} L\left[\frac{1 - cs'}{1 + cs'} \right] \right\}' = -g,$$

and that, if t is in $[0,a]$,

$$s(t) = \frac{m}{k} L\left\{ e\left(\sqrt{\frac{kg}{m}} \, t \right) \right\}$$

or, as frequently written,

$$s(t) = \frac{m}{k} \log \cosh \sqrt{\frac{kg}{m}}\, t.$$

4. A body of mass m is suspended by a spring and the system is in equilibrium. At a certain instant τ, the body is pulled downward a distance h feet and released. Suppose s is the simple graph whose X-projection is the set of nonnegative numbers such that $s(0) = h$, $s'(0) = 0$, and, if t is a positive number, $s(t) = 0$, $s(t) = x$, or $s(t) = -x$ according as the body is at the equilibrium position, below the

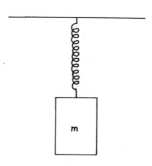

equilibrium position the distance x, or above the equilibrium position the distance x, respectively, at time t after the instant τ. Assume that, if air resistance and friction are neglected, $s'' + k^2 s = 0$, where k is a positive number, and show that, if t is a nonnegative number, $s(t) = h \cdot C(kt)$, or, as frequently written,

$$s(t) = h \cos kt.$$

5. If, in the preceding problem, account is taken of the resistance of the medium in which the system is suspended, the equation for s is $s'' + r^2 s' + k^2 s = \underline{0}$, where r is a positive number. Find s in the case $k^2 > \dfrac{r^2}{4}$.

6. Suppose, finally, that the mechanical system in question is subject to a continuous "impressed force." Then the equation to be solved is $s'' + r^2 s' + k^2 s = g$, where g is a continuous simple graph whose X-projection is the set of nonnegative numbers. Determine s.

FLUID PRESSURE

A region R in a vertical plane is submerged in water. Suppose a is the distance from the water level to the upper boundary of R and b the distance from the water level to the lower boundary of R.

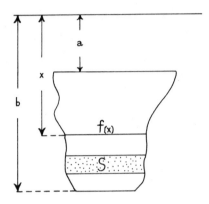

We make the following assumptions:

i. if $[p,q]$ is a subinterval of $[a,b]$, the *pressure* on the strip S, which is the subset of R whose upper and lower boundaries are horizontal and at depths p and q, respectively, is the weight of a column of water of cross section S and height some number between p and q, and

ii. if $S_1 \ldots S_n$ is any finite collection of nonoverlapping strips of this kind filling up R, and P_i is the pressure on S_i, $i = 1 \ldots n$, then the pressure on R is $P_1 + \ldots + P_n$.

Problems

1. Suppose f is the simple graph with X-projection $[a,b]$ such that, for each x in $[a,b]$, $f(x)$ is the width of R measured horizontally at the place the distance x from the water level and $g(x) = \int_a^x f$. Let W denote the density of water. Show that the pressure on R is

$$W \cdot \int_a^b I \, dg.$$

2. A trough of trapezoidal cross-section is 2 feet deep, 2 feet wide at the bottom and 3 feet wide at the top. If the trough is full of water, what is the pressure on the end of the trough?

3. A cylindrical tank 8 feet in diameter is lying on its side. If it

contains water to a depth of 6 feet, find the pressure of the water on one end of the tank.

MOTION IN A PLANE

Suppose $[0,a]$ is an interval and, if t is in $[0,a]$, $(x(t), y(t))$ is a point representing the location of a "particle" in a plane at time t, measured from some instant τ. Each of x and y is a simple graph with X-projection $[0,a]$. The point set to which P belongs only if there is a number t in $[0,a]$ such that $P = (x(t), y(t))$ is the *path* of the motion of the particle and is denoted by $\{x,y\}$. The ordered pair $\{x',y'\}$ is the *velocity* and the ordered pair $\{x'',y''\}$ the *acceleration* of the motion. If t is in $[0,a]$, the number $Q\{[x'(t)]^2 + [y'(t)]^2\}$ is the *speed* or *magnitude of the velocity* at time t and the number $Q\{[x''(t)]^2 + [y''(t)]^2\}$ is the *magnitude of the acceleration* at time t.

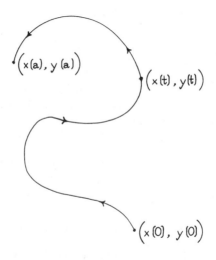

The statement that the path $\{x,y\}$ has *length* means that there exists a number k such that, if D is a finite collection of nonoverlapping intervals filling up $[0,a]$, the sum $\sum Q\{[x(q) - x(p)]^2 + [y(q) - y(p)]^2\}$, formed for all the intervals $[p,q]$ in D, does not exceed k. If $\{x,y\}$ has length and $[u,v]$ is a subinterval of $[0,a]$, the length of $\{x,y\}$ on $[u,v]$, denoted by $\ell_u^v\{x,y\}$, is the least number k such that the above sum formed for any finite collection of nonoverlapping intervals filling up

$[u,v]$ does not exceed k. If $\{x,y\}$ has length on $[0,a]$ and c is a number between 0 and a, then

$$\ell_0^a \{x,y\} = \ell_0^c \{x,y\} + \ell_c^a \{x,y\} \; .$$

If each of x' and y' has X-projection $[0,a]$ and is continuous, then

$$\ell_0^t \{x,y\} = \int_0^t Q[(x')^2 + (y')^2], \; 0 \le t \le a.$$

If we denote this by $s(t)$, then

$$s' = Q[(x')^2 + (y')^2] \, ,$$

so that $s'(t)$ *is the speed of the motion at time t*.

Hypothesis. We suppose x' and y' have X-projection $[0,a]$ and are continuous, and $\{x'(t)\}^2 + \{y'(t)\}^2 > 0$ for every t in $[0,a]$.

Problems

1. Show that there exists only one continuous simple graph θ with X-projection $[0,a]$ such that $0 \le \theta(0) < 2\pi$ and, for each number t in $[0,a]$:

$$x'(t) = s'(t) \cdot \cos \, \theta(t)$$

and

$$y'(t) = s'(t) \cdot \sin \, \theta(t),$$

(*i.e.*, $x' = s'C[\theta]$ and $y' = s'S[\theta]$) .

2. Suppose t_1 and t_2 are numbers in $[0,a]$, $P_1 = (x(t_1), y(t_1))$, $P_2 = (x(t_2), y(t_2))$, $\overline{P_1P_2} = Q\{[x(t_1) - x(t_2)]^2 + [y(t_1) - y(t_2)]^2\}$, the distance from P_1 to P_2, and $\overset{\frown}{P_1P_2} = \left| \int_{t_1}^{t_2} Q[(x')^2 + (y')^2] \right|$, the length of the path between P_1 and P_2. Show that if c is a positive number and t_1 in $[0,a]$, there exists a positive number d such that, if t_2 is in $[0,a]$, is distinct from t_1, and differs from t_1 by less than d, then the quotient

$$\frac{\overline{P_1P_2}}{\overset{\frown}{P_1P_2}}$$

differs from 1 by less than c.

3. Show that if c is a positive number, $0 \le t_1 < a$, then there exists a positive number d such that, if $t_1 < t_2 \le a$ and $t_2 - t_1 < d$, then

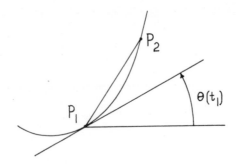

$$\left| \frac{x(t_2) - x(t_1)}{\overline{P_1P_2}} - \cos \theta(t_1) \right| < c$$

and

$$\left| \frac{y(t_2) - y(t_1)}{\overline{P_1P_2}} - \sin \theta(t_1) \right| < c.$$

Thus, the "direction of the motion" at time t_1 is along the tangent line to the path at the point $(x(t_1), y(t_1))$.

4. Suppose t is a number in the X-projection of x'' and in the X-projection of y''. Show that the following statements are true:

(i) $$\theta'(t) = \frac{x'(t)y''(t) - x''(t)y'(t)}{\{s'(t)\}^2} ,$$

(ii) $$s''(t) = x''(t) \cdot \cos \theta(t) + y''(t) \cdot \sin \theta(t),$$

and

(iii) $$s'(t)\theta'(t) = - x''(t) \cdot \sin\theta(t) + y''(t) \cdot \cos \theta(t).$$

If

$$\alpha_m(t) = s''(t) = x''(t) \cdot \cos \theta(t) + y''(t) \cdot \sin \theta(t)$$

and

$$\alpha_n(t) = s'(t) \cdot \theta'(t) = -x''(t) \cdot \sin \theta(t) + y''(t) \cdot \cos \theta(t),$$

we see that the magnitude of the vector $\{\alpha_m(t), \alpha_n(t)\}$ is the magnitude of the acceleration $\{x''(t), y''(t)\}$. The *component* of the acceleration normal (perpendicular) to the path is $\alpha_n(t)$ and the component tangential to the path is $\alpha_m(t)$.

The *curvature* of the path $\{x,y\}$ at the point $(x(t), y(t))$ is

$$\kappa(t) = D_u \, \theta[\sigma],$$

where σ is the simple graph to which the point (p,q) belongs only if (q,p) belongs to s and $\sigma(u) = t$; *i.e.*, $u = s(t)$.

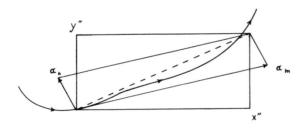

Problems

1. Show that

$$\kappa(t) = \frac{x'(t)y''(t) - x''(t)y'(t)}{\{s'(t)\}^3} .$$

2. Show that the normal component of acceleration is

$$\alpha_n(t) = \kappa(t) \cdot \{s'(t)\}^2 .$$

3. Investigate the motion with path $\{x,y\}$ if $x(0) = 0$, $y(0) = 0$, $x'(0) = v$, $y'(0) = w$, $x'' = \underline{0}$, and $y'' = -g$, where each of v, w, and g is a positive number.

4. Investigate the motion of a place on the rim of a wheel of radius a feet rolling along a straight road making b revolutions per second.

Note. The curvature of a straight line at each of its points is 0. The curvature of a circle at each of its points is the reciprocal of the radius of the circle.

CENTROIDS

The statement that s is the *line interval* with ends P_1 and P_2 means that P_1 and P_2 are points and s is the point set to which P belongs only if there exists a number t in the interval $[0,1]$ such that $P = (1-t) \cdot P_1 + t \cdot P_2$. The statement that the point set M is *convex* means that, if P_1 and P_2 are points of M, the line interval with ends P_1 and P_2 is a subset of M.

Examples. The point set containing only the point P is convex; the set of all points is convex; a line interval is convex; if M_1 and M_2 are convex point sets having a common part M, then M is convex.

Definitions. *The particle of mass m at the point* P is the ordered pair (P,*m*), where P is a point and *m* a nonnegative number.

The statement that (P,*m*) is the *centroid* of the finite set (P₁*m₁*) . . . (P$_n$,*m$_n$*) of particles means that $m = m_1 + \ldots + m_n > 0$ and

$$P = \frac{m_1 \cdot P_1 + \ldots + m_n \cdot P_n}{m_1 + \ldots + m_n} .$$

Note. The point P belongs to the line interval with ends P₁ and P₂ only if there is a particle at P₁ and a particle at P₂ such that the centroid of these two particles is at P.

Problems

1. Suppose r is a positive integer and n a positive integer greater than r, (P₁,*m₁*) . . . (P$_r$,*m$_r$*) has centroid (P'*m'*) and (P$_{r+1}$,*m$_{r+1}$*) . . . (P$_n$,*m$_n$*) has centroid (P'',*m''*). Show that the centroid of (P₁,*m₁*) . . . (P$_n$,*m$_n$*) is the centroid of the two particles (P',*m'*) and (P'',*m''*).

2. Suppose n is a positive integer and P₁ . . . P$_n$ are n points and M the point set to which P belongs only if P is at the centroid of n particles at P₁ . . . P$_n$. Then, M is convex and any convex set which contains P₁ . . . P$_n$ includes M as subset.

3. Extend the preceding considerations to points in space.

Definition. Suppose R is a bounded point set and, for each point P in R, (P,ρ(P)) is a particle at P. The centroid of this set of particles is called the centroid of R with respect to the density function ρ and is the particle (S,*m*) such that

$$m = \iint_R \rho \ dJ \text{ and } S = \frac{\iint_R P\rho \ dJ}{\iint_R \rho \ dJ} \ ,$$

where $\iint_R P\rho \ dJ$ is the point (u,v) such that, if

$$h(x,y) = x \cdot \rho(x,y)$$

and

$$k(x,y) = y \cdot \rho(x,y),$$

then

$$u = \iint_R h \ dJ \text{ and } v = \iint_R k \ dJ.$$

Problems

1. Let R denote the region $[Q;0,1]$ determined by the simple graph Q and the interval $[0,1]$ and let ρ denote the density function defined by $\rho(x,y) = x$. Find the centroid of R with respect to ρ.

2. Find the centroid of the circular disc defined by $x^2 + y^2 \leq 1$ with respect to the density function defined by $\rho(x,y) = 1$.

3. Find the centroid of the quarter circular disc defined by $x^2 + y^2 \leq 1$, $x \geq 0$, $y \geq 0$, with respect to the density function defined by $\rho(x,y) = 1$.

4. Suppose G is a finite collection of nonoverlapping rectangular intervals filling up the rectangular interval $[ab;cd]$, and the region R is a subset of $[ab;cd]$. Suppose $R_1 \ldots R_n$ are the subsets of R included in rectangular intervals of G, and (S_i,m_i) is the centroid of R_i with respect to the density function ρ. Show that the centroid of R with respect to ρ is the centroid of the finite set of particles $(S_1,m_1) \ldots (S_n,m_n)$.

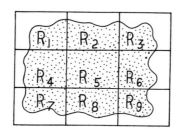

Integral Tables

The statement that F is an antiderivative of the simple graph f means that F is a simple graph such that $F' = f$. If the X-projection of f is an interval and F is an antiderivative of f, then $F + c$, where c is a number, is an antiderivative of f, and there are no others.

A table of "indefinite integrals" is a table of antiderivatives. We denote an antiderivative of the simple graph f by the symbol:

$$\int f.$$

Here are some antiderivatives followed by the corresponding entries in one of several available tables.

1. $\int a = a\mathrm{I}$ $\qquad\qquad \int a\,dx = ax$

7. $\int \mathrm{I}^n = \dfrac{\mathrm{I}^{n+1}}{n+1}$ $\qquad \int x^n\,dx = \dfrac{x^{n+1}}{n+1}$ $\qquad$ (except $n = -1$)

9. $\int \dfrac{1}{\mathrm{I}} = \mathrm{L}[|\mathrm{I}|]$ $\qquad \int \dfrac{dx}{x} = \log x$ or $\log(-x)$

11. $\int \mathrm{E} = \mathrm{E}$ $\qquad\qquad \int e^x = e^x$

12. $\int \mathrm{L} = \mathrm{IL} - \mathrm{I}$ $\qquad \int \log x\,dx = x\log x - x$

16. $\int \dfrac{1}{a^2 + \mathrm{I}^2} = \dfrac{1}{a}\mathrm{A}\!\left[\dfrac{\mathrm{I}}{a}\right]$ $\qquad \int \dfrac{dx}{a^2 + x^2} = \dfrac{1}{a}\tan^{-1}\dfrac{x}{a}$

183. $\int \mathrm{T} = -\mathrm{L}[|\,\mathrm{C}\,|] = $
$\qquad\qquad \mathrm{L}[|\,\mathrm{K}\,|]$ $\qquad \int \tan x\,dx = -\log\cos x = \log\sec x$

187. $\int \mathrm{S}^2 = \dfrac{1}{2}(\mathrm{I} - \mathrm{CS})$ $\qquad \int \sin^2 x\,dx = -\dfrac{1}{2}\sin x\cos x + \dfrac{x}{2}$

202. $\int \dfrac{1}{1 + C} = T\left[\dfrac{I}{2}\right]$ $\int \dfrac{dx}{1 + \cos x} = \tan \dfrac{x}{2}$

244. $\int T^2 = T - I$ $\int \tan^2 x \, dx = \tan x - x$

313. $\int S = \mathcal{C}$ $\int \sinh x \, dx = \cosh x$

In using the tables, it is necessary to supply the range on which the formulas are valid. For instance, if $n = \frac{1}{2}$ in No. 7, the formula is valid for all nonnegative numbers but not for negative numbers.

Index of Simple Graphs

Unless otherwise stated, the following letters denote certain specific simple graphs:

H, L, E, Q, I, S, $\mathcal{C}$, $\mathcal{T}$, $\mathcal{K}$, $\mathcal{A}$, Ω, A, T, K, C, S, B, as follows.

Symbol	Meaning	Page
H	(x,y) belongs to H only if x is a positive number and $y = \dfrac{1}{x}$	14
L	(x,y) belongs to L only if x is a positive number and $y = \int_1^x H$	17
E	(x,y) belongs to E only if (y,x) belongs to L	21
Q	(x,y) belongs to Q only if x is a nonnegative number and $y = \sqrt{x}$	23
I	(x,y) belongs to I only if x is a number and $y = x$	32
S	$S = \dfrac{1}{2}\left\{ E - \dfrac{1}{E} \right\}$	40
$\mathcal{C}$	$\mathcal{C} = \dfrac{1}{2}\left\{ E + \dfrac{1}{E} \right\}$	40
$\mathcal{T}$	$\mathcal{T} = \dfrac{S}{\mathcal{C}}$	41

Symbol	Meaning	Page
$\varkappa$	$\varkappa = \dfrac{1}{\mathcal{C}}$	41
$\mathcal{A}$	(x,y) belongs to $\mathcal{A}$ only if (y,x) belongs to $\mathcal{C}$	41
Ω	$\Omega = \dfrac{1}{1 + \mathrm{I}^2}$	44
A	(x,y) belongs to A only if x is a number and $$A(x) = \int_0^x \Omega$$	44
T	(x,y) belongs to T only if $-\dfrac{\pi}{2} < x < \dfrac{\pi}{2}$ and (y,x) belongs to A or there is a number t between $-\dfrac{\pi}{2}$ and $\dfrac{\pi}{2}$ and an integer n such that $x = t + n\pi$ and $A(x) = A(t)$	47
K	$K^2 = 1 + T^2$, $K(x) > 0$ if $-\dfrac{\pi}{2} < x < \dfrac{\pi}{2}$, $K(x) < 0$ if $\dfrac{\pi}{2} < x < \dfrac{3\pi}{2}$ and if there is a number t distinct from $\dfrac{\pi}{2}$ between $-\dfrac{\pi}{2}$ and $\dfrac{3\pi}{2}$ and an integer n such that $x = t + 2n\pi$, then $K(x) = K(t)$	50
C	If x is the abscissa of a point of K, then $C(x) = \dfrac{1}{K(x)}$ and, otherwise, $C(x) = 0$	50
S	If x is the abscissa of a point of T, $S(x) = C(x)T(x)$ and, if n is an integer, $S\left\{\dfrac{(2n-1)\pi}{2}\right\} = (-1)^{n-1}$.	50
B	(x,y) belongs to B only if y is in the interval $\left[-\dfrac{\pi}{2}, \dfrac{\pi}{2}\right]$ and $x = S(y)$	51

Glossary of Definitions

The statement that:	Means:
(x,y) *is a point*	(x,y) is an ordered number pair
x is the *abscissa* of the point P	x is the first or left-most number of P
y is the *ordinate* of the point P	y is the second or right-most number of P
S is a *point set*	S is a collection of one or more points
f is a *simple graph*	f is a point set no two points of which have the same abscissa
$f(x)$ is f *of* x	$f(x)$ is the ordinate of that point of the simple graph f whose abscissa is x
M is the X-*projection* of the point set S	M is the number set to which x belongs only if x is the abscissa of a point of S
$[a,b]$ is an interval	a and b are numbers, $a < b$ and $[a,b]$ is the number set to which x belongs only if x is a, x is b, or x is a number between a and b
$[f;a,b]$ is the *region* determined by the simple graph f and the interval $[a,b]$	the X-projection of f includes $[a,b]$ and $[f;a,b]$ is the point set to which (x,y) belongs only if x is in $[a,b]$ and y is 0, y is $f(x)$, or y is a number between 0 and $f(x)$

$\underline{h}$ (read "h horizontal") is a horizontal line	h is a number and $\underline{h}$ is the point set to which (x,y) belongs only if x is a number and y is h
x is an *end* of the interval $[a,b]$	x is a or x is b
G is a collection of non-overlapping intervals	G is a collection of one or more intervals and, if two intervals in G have a number in common, this number is an end of each of them
S is a *finite* set	there is a positive integer n such that S does not contain n elements
S is an *infinite* set	if n is a positive integer, S contains n elements
S is an *inner sum* for the region $[H;a,b]$	there exists a finite collection G of non-overlapping intervals filling up $[a,b]$ such that, if the length of each interval $[p,q]$ in G is multiplied by $\frac{1}{q}$, the sum of all the products so formed is S
$\int_a^b$ H is the *area* of the region $[H;a,b]$	$\int_a^b$ H is the least number which no inner sum for $[H;a,b]$ exceeds
g is the straight line of slope m containing the point (a,b)	m is a number and g is the simple graph to which (x,y) belongs only if x is a number and $y = m(x - a) + b$
$\log_a x$ is the logarithm of x to the base a	a is a positive number distinct from 1, x is a positive number and $\log_a x = \dfrac{L(x)}{L(a)}$
a is the number e	a is the positive number such that $L(a) = 1$
a^x is a *to the* x	x is a number and $a^x = E\{xL(a)\}$
$|x|$ is the *absolute* value of x	x is a number and $|x| = Q(x^2)$

185

$h\|$, read h *vertical*, is a vertical line	h is a number and $h\|$ is the point set to which (x,y) belongs only if y is a number and x is h
the simple graph f has *slope* at the point P	P is a point of f such that each two vertical lines with P between them have between them a point of f distinct from P and there exists a number m, called the *slope* of f at P, such that, if α is a straight line containing P of slope greater than m and β is a straight line containing P of slope less than m, then there exist two vertical lines $h\|$ and $k\|$ with P between them such that every point of f between $h\|$ and $k\|$ distinct from P is between α and β
g is the *tangent line* to the simple graph f at the point P	f has slope m at P and g is the straight line of slope m containing P
$f+g$ is the *sum* of the simple graph f and the simple graph g	the X-projection of f and the X-projection of g have a common part and, if x is in this common part, $(f+g)(x)=f(x)+g(x)$
$f\cdot g$ or fg is the *product* of the simple graph f and the simple graph g	the X-projection of f and the X-projection of g have a common part and, if x is in this common part, $(f\cdot g)(x)=f(x)g(x)$
$f[g]$ is the *bracket product* f of g	there is a number x such that $g(x)$ is in the X-projection of f and, if x is such a number, $f[g](x)=f\{g(x)\}$
$\dfrac{1}{g}$ is the *reciprocal* of the simple graph g	there is a number x such that $g(x) \neq 0$ and, if x is such a number, $\dfrac{1}{g}(x)=\dfrac{1}{g(x)}$
$\dfrac{f}{g}$ is the *quotient* of the simple graph f by the simple graph g (or over g)	$\dfrac{f}{g}=f\cdot\dfrac{1}{g}$

f' is the *derivative* of the simple graph f	there is a number x such that f has slope at $(x, f(x))$ and, for any such x, $f'(x)$ is the slope of f at $(x, f(x))$
s is the *segment* with ends a and b	a and b are numbers and s is the number set to which x belongs only if x is between a and b
the simple graph f has property (S) at P (or is *continuous* at P)	P is a point of f such that, if α and β are horizontal lines with P between them, there exist vertical lines $h\|$ and $k\|$ with P between them such that every point of f between $h\|$ and $k\|$ is between α and β
$g\|_a^b$ is the *g-length* of the interval $[a,b]$	g is a simple graph whose X-projection includes $[a,b]$ and $g\|_a^b = g(b) - g(a)$
g is *nondecreasing* on $[a,b]$	the X-projection of the simple graph g includes $[a,b]$ and the g-length of every subinterval of $[a,b]$ is nonnegative
g is *increasing* on $[a,b]$	the X-projection of the simple graph g includes $[a,b]$ and the g-length of every subinterval of $[a,b]$ is positive
F is a *transformation* from the set A to the set B	F is a collection of ordered pairs (a,b) whose left-most element a is in A, whose right-most element b is in B, such that each element of A is the first element of *only one* ordered pair in F and each element of B is the second element of *some* ordered pair in F
f is g-integrable on $[a,b]$	each of f and g is a simple graph whose X-projection includes the interval $[a,b]$ and there exists a number J, called the integral from a to b of f with respect to g and denoted by $\int_a^b f\,dg$, such that, if c is a positive number, there exists a finite collection D of nonoverlapping intervals

	filling up $[a,b]$ such that, if D′ is a finite collection of nonoverlapping intervals filling up $[a,b]$ with each end of each interval of D an end of some interval of D′ and the g-length of each interval of D′ is multiplied by the ordinate of any point of f whose abscissa is in that interval, then the sum of all the products so formed differs from J by less than c
f is a simple surface	f is a transformation from a point set to a number set
$[ab;cd]$ is a rectangular interval	$[a,b]$ is an interval, $[c,d]$ is an interval and $[ab;cd]$ is the point set to which (x,y) belongs only if x belongs to $[a,b]$ and y to $[c,d]$
R is the *edge* of the rectangular interval $[ab;cd]$	R is the point set to which (x,y) belongs only if (x,y) belongs to $[ab;cd]$ and $x=a$, $x=b$, $y=c$, or $y=d$
s is a *rectangular segment*	s is a rectangular interval minus its edge
the simple surface f is continuous at $(P,f(P))$	if c is a positive number, there exists a rectangular segment s containing P such that, if Q is a point in s and in the XY-projection of f, then $f(P)$ differs from $f(Q)$ by less than c
f'_1 is the 1-derivative of the simple surface f	f'_1 is the simple surface to which $((x,y),z)$ belongs only if $z = D_x f[I,y]$
f'_2 is the 2-derivative of the simple surface f	f'_2 is the simple surface to which $((x,y),z)$ belongs only if $z = D_y f[x,I]$
f''_{ij} is the ij-derivative of the simple surface f	$f''_{ij} = (f'_i)'_j \qquad (i=1,2,\ j=1,2)$

the simple surface f has gradient at $(P, f(P))$, $P = (x,y)$	there exists only one ordered number pair $\{p,q\}$ [called the gradient of f at $(P, f(P))$] such that, if c is a positive number, there exists a rectangular segment s containing P such that, if (u,v) is a point of s in the XY-projection of f, then $$f(u,v) - f(x,y) = p \cdot (u - x) + q \cdot (v - y)$$ $$+ \, |P - (u,v)| \cdot \begin{bmatrix} \text{a number between} \\ -c \text{ and } c \end{bmatrix}$$
$g\big\|_a^b\big\|_c^d$ is the g-area of the rectangular interval $[ab; cd]$	g is a simple surface whose XY-projection includes $[ab; cd]$ and $g\big\|_a^b\big\|_c^d = \{g[b,\text{I}] - g[a,\text{I}]\}\big\|_c^d = g(b,d) - g(a,d) - g(b,c) + g(a,c)$